Technological Innovation and the Decorative Arts

AN EXHIBITION AT THE HAGLEY MUSEUM
COSPONSORED BY
THE HENRY FRANCIS DU PONT WINTERTHUR MUSEUM

*Technological Innovation and the
Decorative Arts*
An Exhibition at The Hagley Museum
March 29 through December 30, 1973
cosponsored by The Hagley Museum
and The Henry Francis du Pont
Winterthur Museum

Table of Contents

Foreword

With few notable exceptions the subject of the interplay of technology and the decorative arts has lacked the investigation it deserves. The increasing overspecialization of the academic world threatens to abandon this age-old "chicken and egg" question still further. Art historical monographs on the beauty of line and the origin of design proliferate, while their authors often lack adequate knowledge or curiosity to investigate the technology that produced the products they admire. Historians of technology, on the other hand, sometimes purposefully neglect the artifact—the product of their beloved technology—as a foible of the connoisseur and dilettante. A marriage of the two disciplines, although obvious and seemingly inevitable, has too long been in the making. One notable exception to this scholastic narrowness is Cyril Stanley Smith, who, originally trained as a metallurgist, spans the two disciplines and has done much to publicize the intimate link of art and technology and their simultaneous origins.

It was the 1973 Winterthur Conference entitled "Technological Innovation and the Decorative Arts," with Cyril Stanley Smith as its keynote speaker, that brought together leading authorities of both disciplines in an innovative interdisciplinary investigation.* The geographical proximity of The Hagley Museum, a museum devoted to the history of technology, provided an exceptional opportunity for a cosponsored exhibit drawing on Winterthur's outstanding collection of American decorative arts as a complement to the conference theme. Thus, the seed was sown for a joint exhibition utilizing the talents of both institutions to explore three-dimensionally "Technological Innovation and the Decorative Arts."

*The proceedings of the Winterthur Conference are available in Ian M. G. Quimby, ed., *Technological Innovation and the Decorative Arts* (Charlottesville: University Press of Virginia, 1973).

From its inception, the exhibit was conceived as a practicum for students in the graduate training programs of both museums and the nearby University of Delaware museum training program. The exhibit presented an ideal opportunity to experience all aspects of exhibit technique. The exhibit was researched, planned, designed, and mounted by students with the aid of the professional staffs of the cosponsoring institutions and with the generous assistance of the speakers at the 1973 Winterthur Conference whose paper topics formed the basis for the exhibit. Special appreciation is extended to the following conference speakers: Catherine Lynn Frangiamore, Assistant Curator, Cooper-Hewitt Museum of Decorative Arts & Design (The Smithsonian Institution); John D. Tyler, Curator of Science, Industry, and Technology, William Penn Memorial Museum; Kenneth M. Wilson, Chief Curator, The Corning Museum of Glass; and Florence M. Montgomery, New Haven, Connecticut.

The overall aim of the exhibit was to explore the interplay of technology and design in the era of man's increasing exploitation of the machine. The viewer is purposefully presented with no preconceived statement but is invited to explore the question for himself. Where inconsistencies in design and philosophy are evident, they are the product of the exploratory and teaching nature of the exhibit. Specific subject areas of the exhibit were prepared by different groups of students with only minimal interchange of ideas, and every attempt was made to allow the students as much latitude as possible. While only a superficial examination of the subject was possible, it is hoped that the exhibit will serve as an inspiration for further investigations.

Students in the Hagley Fellowship Program, the Winterthur Program in Early American Culture, and the University of Delaware Museum Studies Program were responsible for the following subject areas: FURNITURE: Ellen Kirven and Page E. Talbott; CLOCKS AND GUNS: Thomas C. Guider, L. Corwin Sharp, and Gregory R. Weidman; WALLPAPER: Deborah D. Waters and Sally Schwartz; IRON: John H. Demer, Carlene Evans Stephens, and Kathy Kresge; GLASS: David E. Nathans, Christina H. Nelson, Anne B. Spivey, and Robert F. Trent; TEXTILES: Linda Lounsbury, Lois L. Olcott, and Rosemary E. Troy; SILVER: Ann Brown, Margaret R. Burke, David A. Hounshell, and Wendy C. Wick. The exhibit committee also wishes to acknowledge August W. Giebelhaus and Duane P. Swanson for their assistance whenever and wherever it was needed; Deborah Waters for her work on the overall design; Rosemary Troy and Anne Spivey for their continuing interest and assistance in catalogue preparation; and the Hagley Museum exhibit staff for their support in all stages of exhibit preparation.

We extend special thanks to our lenders: Jane W. Anderson; American Precision Museum, Inc.; Louise C. Belden; Joseph T. Butler; Colonial Williamsburg, Inc.; Cooper-Hewitt Museum of Decorative Arts & Design (The Smithsonian Institution); The Corning Museum of Glass; A. L. Diament & Company; Charles B. Gardner; Reaves F. Goehring, Jr.; John H. Hill; Hopewell Village National Historic Site (National Park Service); Independence National Historical Park (National Park Service); Samuel Kirk & Son; Edward F. La Fond, Jr.; Dwight P. Lanmon; Betty-Bright P. Low; Museum of the City of New York; The National Museum of History and Technology (The Smithsonian Institution); Old Salem, Inc.; Pennsylvania Farm Museum of Landis Valley; Pennsylvania Historical & Museum Commission; Dr. Harry J. Repman; The Sandwich Glass Museum; Esther Schwartz; Springfield Armory Museum, Inc. Lastly, the National Endowment for the Humanities Museum Program generously funded the exhibition project.

The catalogue reproduces the explanatory text installed in the exhibit largely unchanged, and all the objects and graphic materials displayed are listed in the numbered catalogue entries. Although it is impossible to recreate in photographs the effect of the working machinery and processes in the exhibit, among them textile printing by hand and electroplating, the illustrations selected for reproduction here are intended to convey the wide variety of machines, processes, and products depicted in the exhibit and their interrelationships. All objects are credited to their owners, and objects from the collections of the Hagley and Winterthur museums are identified HM and WM respectively.

EXHIBIT COMMITTEE
Maureen O'Brien Quimby, Coordinator
Polly Anne Earl
Eugene Ferguson
Ian M. G. Quimby

Introduction

"Technological Innovation and the Decorative Arts" is an exhibit designed to suggest through a few selected examples the impact of the industrial revolution on home furnishings. The examples selected represent familiar objects: furniture, wallpaper, printed textiles, glass tableware, clocks, silver, domestic iron, and guns. When these objects were handcrafted they were expensive, and the average person could never expect to own more than a limited selection.

The nineteenth century inaugurated revolutionary changes in the production of home furnishings. New machines and new processes as well as modification and rediscovery of older processes led to enormous increases in productivity, which in turn lowered the cost of individual items. Inventions like the Blanchard lathe, the mortising machine, and the carving machine eliminated the hand labor needed to reproduce complex forms and ornate decoration in guns and furniture. Principles once discovered were quickly adapted for use in seemingly unrelated industries. The tracing principle of the Blanchard lathe was readily adapted to carving machines and metal engraving pantographs. New techniques of casting and pressing permitted large-scale production of elaborate designs in materials like iron and glass. Mechanized printing presses introduced a new variety of patterns and colors in the motifs of now inexpensive wallpaper and fabrics. The discovery of electrolysis spawned the new industry of electroplated silver, whose products lent an air of opulence to the average home.

Much of Victorian "clutter" was not just a matter of fashion; it was an aesthetic of plenty that owed its existence to the new industrial cornucopia. Although good design was often subordinated to the demands of quantity production, many products of the period reflect an exuberant sense of experimentation in novel forms and materials. While the newly spawned machine abundance infiltrated every aspect of life, the individual production of the craftsman and artist, aided in varying degrees by technology, was never lost to a certain segment of society. In the final analysis, technological innovation democratized the decorative arts by bringing an abundance of domestic furnishings within the reach of nearly everyone.

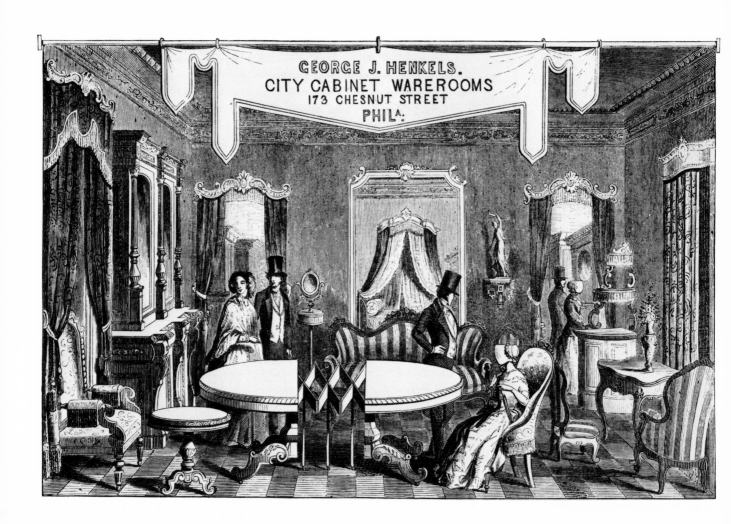

I. Furniture: Mass-Produced and Custom-Made

Expanding population and markets combined with the introduction of machine technology allowed nineteenth-century cabinetmakers to increase the number and variety of their products. Whether powered by foot or by steam, devices such as saws, mortising machines, and wood-carving machines were the key to a vastly increased output of furniture. Quantity production and improved methods of distribution brought a great variety of furniture within the reach of the average family. New techniques and adaptations of old ones freed craftsmen from the traditional limitations of their basic material, wood, and allowed them to use new and old materials in unusual ways. Steam bending and lamination presented novel possibilities in wood shaping and decoration. The plasticity of papier-mâché made unusual, irregular forms possible.

The search for effective but inexpensive substitutes for handwork provided an impetus toward mechanization in furniture-making. Joining furniture parts with a hand-cut mortise and tenon was a traditional method of furniture construction, but a foot-pedal mortising machine (1, illustrated) decreased the time needed to hand-chisel a mortise and also made a more accurate hole. Although machines were neither technologically elaborate nor expensive, an 1836 commentator claimed that "With ordinary care, and a few hours' experience, any man can perform as much labor in one day, with this machine, as in a whole week in the ordinary mode...and...probably...the owners of them have, on an average saved twice the cost of them."*

The plain surfaces and uninterrupted silhouettes of the pillar and scroll style furniture, popular in the 1840s and 50s, are often

*"Mortising Machine," *Mechanics' Magazine and Journal of the Mechanics' Institute* 8, no. 1 (July 1836) : 7.

9

associated with the introduction of laborsaving machinery, but in fact the sweeping outlines of pillar and scroll pieces allowed a saving in production costs whether made by hand or by machine. The plainness of pillar and scroll pieces, like the miniature child's sofa (2, illustrated), was often offset by applied veneers with highly figured patterns. In addition to providing pattern and color, veneers of expensive woods in sheets large enough to cover entire pieces of furniture helped to give the appearance of luxury at less cost. By the 1820s steam- and waterpowered saws adapted to cutting thin sheets of veneer were replacing the careful hand cutting of the eighteenth century. By the 1870s circular saws could cut up to fourteen sheets of veneer from an inch of wood, twice as many as could be cut by hand.

Saws were also important in other processes of furniture production. Jig, or scroll, saws with reciprocating blades could be adapted to human or mechanical power (3, illustrated). Cabinetmakers used jigsaws to produce infinite variations on the perforated designs so commonly associated with Victorian styles. The same kind of saw could be used to replace hand labor on cheap furniture, or it could be used as an adjunct to hand work on expensive furniture. John Henry Belter, one of the best known furniture makers of the period, used this type of machine to produce the basic incisions for his chair back designs, which were then carved by hand. On inexpensive furniture flat, two-dimensional carving was often done by machine, but Belter's furniture was relatively elaborate and expensive. Belter also developed new pressing and forming techniques for working with wood. His 1858 patent applied an old principle, lamination, to fabricate wood that would accept the bending and carving characteristic of his work. Belter's two-step process employed several layers of laminated strips of wood, called staves, which were placed around a mold and pressed into a curved shape by the exterior sections of the mold. When heated and cooled the now solid wood form was cut apart to yield a number of chair backs. Belter's method produced lighter, stronger curved forms and effected a saving in material costs (4, illustrated). Belter claimed his innovations resulted in "work...more graceful in appearance and better adapted in form to its intended use than ordinary pressed work, and . . . much stronger and stiffer."

Another form of pressed work used in the nineteenth century relied on papier-mâché as a basic material. Papier-mâché con-

Mortising machine, overall and detail of bed and chisel with workpiece. Late 1880s, America; H. 58½".

2 · *Child's sofa* (mahogany).
1820-40, New Hampshire; H. 17".

struction gave the craftsman increased flexibility in the decoration and shaping of furniture. Composition materials such as papier-mâché, plaster, and sawdust were frequently pressed in molds to make architectural ornaments or decorations applied to furniture. But the potential of such molding processes is more fully realized in twentieth-century plastic furniture.

Steam bending of wood, a process long used in shaping the curved wooden forms of barrels and boats, is an example of a technique allowing the craftsman to realize the aesthetic potential of his materials. Samuel Gragg of Boston was the first in America to refine and adapt this process to produce sophisticated yet inexpensive furniture such as his "elastic chair" (8, illustrated).

The coordination of technique, machine, and laborer in an assembly line was perhaps the most important contribution of nineteenth-century technology. Efforts to develop effective systems of machine production began early in the century. At Hitchcocksville, Connecticut, the combination of water-powered machines used at the factory (lathes, planers, and mortising machines) and an effective assembly-line system resulted in low-cost quantity production (9, illustrated). No longer did householders have to order individual chairs from cabinetmakers; instead factory-made chairs became a ready-made product stocked by retail merchants.

1 *Mortising machine shown with workpiece.* Late 1880s, America; H. 58½″. By the 1830s simple machines like this had been introduced to speed basic processes in furniture joinery. (HM: Illustrated)

2 *Child's sofa* (mahogany). 1820-40, New Hampshire; H. 17″, W. 31⅝″, D. 13¾″. This pillar and scroll sofa covered in hand-sawn veneers represents a type of furniture more often made with power machinery. (WM: Illustrated)

3 *Jigsaw with drill attachment,* Trump Bros. Nineteenth century, Wilmington, Delaware; H. 42″. A foot-operated example of a common woodworking shop machine. This type of jigsaw was patented in 1876. Painted mark, "Dexter.C." (HM, gift of Henry Neel estate: Illustrated)

4 *Slipper chair* (laminated rosewood), attributed to John H. Belter. 1855, New York City; H. 44″, W. 17½″, D. 18″. This chair, an example of the rococo revival style popular in Victorian America, is also an example of Belter's use of the well-known techniques of laminating and bending to introduce new forms and uses for wood. (Courtesy Joseph T. Butler: Illustrated)

5 *Side chair* (japanned, papier-mâché, mother-of-pearl, wood). About 1850, probably America; H. 33½″, W. 16″, D. 16″. Fragile furniture made of pressed papier-mâché, with japanned decoration to simulate Oriental lacquer work, was produced largely in Europe, although a few examples were made in America. The entire chair back is made of papier-mâché. (Courtesy Museum of the City of New York)

6 *Mold for casting ornamental trim* and modern plastic cast. 1800-50, America; H. 11″. This mold was for casting architectural ornament, but the technique was also used to make decorative elements for furniture. (Courtesy Dwight P. Lanmon)

7 *Slat-bending clamp,* Nathaniel Dominy V. 1800-40, East Hampton, Long Island; L. 27″. The clamp is an example of an early type of hand tool used to shape chair parts. After being steamed, or immersed in hot water, the slats became flexible and were placed in the clamp, which held the slat in a curved shape until it dried. (WM, funds for purchase, gift of Henry Belin du Pont)

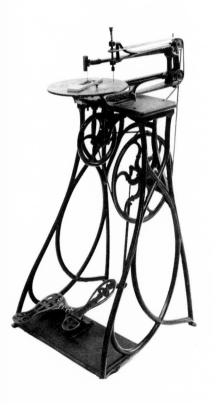

3 *Jigsaw,* Trump Bros. Nineteenth century, Wilmington, Delaware; H. 42″.

8 *Side chair* (birch, white oak, beech), Samuel Gragg. 1808-13, Boston; H. 34⅜″, W. 18⅛″, D. 25⅜″. Labeled "S. Gragg/Boston/Patent." An early innovative use of wood-bending techniques to form an entire chair. (WM: Illustrated)

9 *Side chair* (birch, beech), Hitchcock, Alford Co. 1829-43, Hitchcocksville, Connecticut; H. 34⅝″, W. 17⅜″, D. 13¾″. Labeled. Typical of chairs made at the Hitchcock furniture factory, this chair retailed for $1.50. (WM: Illustrated)

10 *Barnes patent foot-power machinery.* From *The American Furniture Gazette,* n. ser. 3, no. 10 (Nov. 1, 1889): 35.

11 *Interior view of furniture factory.* From *Michigan Artisan* 12, no. 10 (Apr. 15, 1892): inset opposite 16.

12 *Mock-up of veneering saw* based on plate 9 from J. Richards, "Wood-working Machinery," *Journal of the Franklin Institute,* 3rd ser. 62, no. 5 (Nov. 1871).

13 *Drawing* from John H. Belter, "Improvement in the Method of Manufacturing Furniture," U.S. Patent no. 19,405, Feb. 23, 1858.

14 *Modern mortise and tenon.* (Constructed for exhibit)

15 *Trade label of George J. Henkels.* About 1850, Philadelphia. Winterthur Museum Libraries 66 x 95.

16 *Trade label of George J. Henkels.* 1850s, Philadelphia. Winterthur Museum Libraries 66 x 118.1. (Cover Illustration)

4 *Slipper chair,* attributed to John H. Belter. 1855, New York City; H. 44".

8 *Side chair,* Samuel Gragg. 1808-13, Boston; H. 34⅜".

9 *Side chair,* Hitchcock, Alford Co. 1829-43, Hitchcocksville, Connecticut; H. 34⅝".

II. Wallpaper Printing: By Hand and By Machine

Beginning in the 1760s, wallpaper manufactured in America joined paper imported from England and France on the colonial market. Before the Revolution, block printers were at work in New York City and Philadelphia. During the eighteenth century, techniques for block printing wallpaper improved, yet reliance on paper made and printed by hand, in a single sheet, kept prices high (2, illustrated).

By 1807 development of the Fourdrinier machine, which produced endless rolls of paper, allowed the introduction of cylinder-printing presses adapted from the textile industry for machine printing wallpaper. However, not until the 1840s, did Howell and Brothers of Philadelphia import wallpaper-printing machinery. Within twenty years, the increase in production following mechanization had become a boom, which was spurred by the availability of the inexpensive wood-pulp paper that replaced rag paper after the Civil War.

Wallpaper printing, by hand or by machine, involves two major steps: preparing the paper to receive color and printing the paper with successive colors and details. Before hand printing, paper surfaces must be sized, or treated with glue, to hold pigments. When liquid colors are used, the glue is applied first; when earth colors (mineral pigments) are used, they are premixed with glue and both are applied at once. When the paper is dry, the first color, the ground, usually gray or the darkest blue of the sky, is painted on. Working on a long table, a workman spreads the color the full length of the paper. To make certain the color is even, he is followed by two sweepers. After being dried and polished on the back, the paper is ready for printing.

Wood blocks for hand printing consist of several layers of wood glued together like modern plywood. The surface layer, on which the design is carved, is a hard, dense wood such as pearwood (5, illustrated). The printer applies color to the wood block by lower-

The Twelve-Color Printing Machine. From *Artistic Wall Papers Designed and Manufactured by Fr. Beck & Co.* (New York: New York and Brooklyn Publishing Co., 1881).

17

ing the block onto the color-soaked felt pad of the color tub. The block is applied to the paper under pressure to give even distribution of the color. The largest color areas are printed first; other colors are applied working from dark to light. Details are printed last.

The techniques of preparing and printing paper by machine are similar to hand-printing processes. The paper rolls are prepared by a machine called the "blotcher" in which a series of brushes apply the ground color over the entire surface. After drying and reeling, the paper is ready for printing. Rollers arranged in sequence in a cylinder press replace the wood blocks of hand printing. The design for each color is drawn on transfer paper, which is wrapped around the roller while the ink is still wet. A workman called the block cutter cuts the ink lines of the design into the roller and then inserts strips of brass to create a raised brass outline of the pattern. Where solid colors are desired, felt is fitted into the brass outline (8, illustrated). In 1888 a set of rollers cost about $500 and required from six to twelve weeks to produce.*

In the printing machine, grounded paper passes between the impression cylinder and the small pattern rollers. Color is conveyed to the face of each pattern roller by endless sieve cloths supplied by color boxes, one box and one cloth for each color. By the 1880s, eight- and twelve-color machines were quite common (30, illustrated). As the paper emerges from the machine, it is caught on sticks resting in notches on an endless chain, and it is carried over steam pipes for rapid drying.

In addition to the printing press, machines were developed to produce special effects previously achieved by hand labor. By the early eighteenth century, English manufacturers were producing flocked wall coverings in bold, sumptuous designs. Flock, finely chopped fibers of wool or silk, was applied to paper or canvas that had previously been printed or stenciled in a pattern with glue or varnish. Part of the flock adhered to the sticky portions of the ground; the remainder was shaken off to reveal the pattern.

In the nineteenth-century flocking process, flock was dusted over paper laid in a tray with an elastic bottom. Boys then beat

8 *Wallpaper rollers* (wood, metal, and felt), probably F. E. James Company. 1850-65, America; approx. L. 21½″, Diam. 5¼″.

*"A Visit to Janeway and Carpenter's Factory, New Brunswick, N.J.," *The Painters Magazine and Wall Paper Trade Journal* (Dec. 1888): 654-55.

the bottom of the tray to ensure even distribution of the flock. Plain unpatterned flocked papers were easily produced by machines that applied varnish and beat the paper with steam-driven mechanical fingers. In the 1880s American wallpaper factories produced quantities of flocked or "velvet" papers.

With the introduction of machines for embossing, gilding, and flocking papers, good design was frequently subordinated to novel effects. By the 1880s, "papers for the finest and most costly mansion, and papers for the little nest of a cottage," were available at prices ranging from 25¢ to $12 a roll, "thus suiting all purses and tastes."* Such widespread availability intensified the role of wallpaper as a carrier of decorative styles across the nation (14, illustrated).

But increasing demand for new patterns throughout the nineteenth century generated products that drew criticism for their poor design. In reaction, designers like William Morris revived the tradition of fine hand-printed papers. At their best, nineteenth-century American wallpapers offered examples of successful flat-pattern design adapted either to the demands of machine production and mass distribution, or to the continuation of fine block printing on a limited scale.

5 *Wood block for strip 1 of scenic paper, "Vues de l'Amerique du Nord."* First printed by Zuber, 1834, Rixheim, Alsace; approx. L. 19", W. 17¼".

*"The Manufacture of Wallpapers," *Scientific American,* n. ser. 45, no. 22 (Nov. 26, 1881) : 335.

1 *Block print.* 1750, France; approx. L. 19¼″, W. 12½″. Domino pattern with stenciled washes in brown, yellow, and blue. (Courtesy Cooper-Hewitt Museum of Decorative Arts & Design)

2 *Block print, "Les Deux Pigeons,"* Jean-Baptiste Reveillon. About 1783, Paris; approx. L. 46¾″, W. 20½″. Two pigeons among flowers of red, green, gray, and yellow on a blue background. French wallpapers of this period were more skillfully printed and better colored than American. (Courtesy Cooper-Hewitt Museum of Decorative Arts & Design: Illustrated)

3 *Block print* (joined sheets). About 1765, England; approx. L. 27¼″, W. 20¼″. Green flowers on a green stenciled background. This paper, from the Jeremiah Lee Mansion, Marblehead, Massachusetts, has a British excise stamp on the reverse. (Courtesy Cooper-Hewitt Museum of Decorative Arts & Design)

4 *Wood block for strip 1 of scenic paper, "Vues de l'Amerique du Nord."* First printed by Zuber, 1834, Rixheim, Alsace; approx. L. 19″, W. 17¼″. (Courtesy A. L. Diament & Company)

5 *Wood block for strip 1 of scenic paper, "Vues de l'Amerique du Nord."* First printed by Zuber, 1834, Rixheim, Alsace; approx. L. 19″, W. 19″. (Courtesy A. L. Diament & Company: Illustrated)

6 *Wood block for strip 24 of scenic paper, "Les Grandes Chasses."* First printed in 1831, France; L. 13½″, W. 5¾″. The original view was painted by Jean Julien Deltil. (Courtesy A. L. Diament & Company)

7 *Wood block* (wood and brass) for border pattern with swags. 1860-70, France; approx. L. 24″, W. 9″. (Courtesy Cooper-Hewitt Museum of Decorative Arts & Design)

8 *Wallpaper rollers* (wood, metal, and felt), probably F. E. James Company. 1850-65, America; approx. L. 21½″, Diam. 5¼″. Unlike textile-printing rollers, which printed color from engraved lines, wallpaper-printing rollers printed color from raised lines or surfaces. (Courtesy Cooper-Hewitt Museum of Decorative Arts & Design: Illustrated)

9a-c *Paper layers from the parlor of the General Philip Schuyler summer house,* Schuylerville, New York. The successive layers of paper from Schuyler's parlor give an indication of changing tastes in the mid-nineteenth century. (Courtesy Independence National Historical Park)

Block print, "Les Deux Pigeons,"
Jean-Baptiste Reveillon. About
1783, Paris; approx. L. 46¾ ″,
W. 20½ ″.

9a *Block print* (wove paper), Anthony Chardon. 1814-25, Philadelphia; approx. L. 9¾″, W. 10″. Brown leaves and berries on an off-white background. This paper, stamped on the reverse with the maker's name, is the third layer removed from the parlor.

9b *Block print* (laid paper). Mid-nineteenth century; approx. L. 18½″, W. 16½″. A swag and floral design in pink and green formed the middle section of the fourth layer.

9c *Machine print* (laid paper). Mid-nineteenth century; approx. L. 9″, W. 18″. Brown, green, and gold flowers border a vertical, stenciled design in green from the middle section of the fifth layer.

10 *Flocked block print* (joined sheets). Mid-eighteenth century, England; approx. L. 52½″, W. 21⅛″. Yellow and gold flowers and swag design. (Courtesy Cooper-Hewitt Museum of Decorative Arts & Design)

11 *Machine print* (wood-pulp stock). Late nineteenth century, America; approx. L. 18″, W. 18″. Gold and red fleurs-de-lis on beige background. (Courtesy Cooper-Hewitt Museum of Decorative Arts & Design)

12 *Machine print* (wood-pulp stock). Late nineteenth century, America; approx. L. 25½″, W. 18¾″. Gold and green fleurs-de-lis on a brown background. (Courtesy Cooper-Hewitt Museum of Decorative Arts & Design)

13 *Machine print*. 1880-90, America; approx. L. 23″, W. 18″. Metallic gold floral pattern in relief on maroon ground. This imitation leather wall covering from the dining room of the John D. Rockefeller house, New York City, is probably Lincrusta Walton, a brand name product based on linseed oil. (Courtesy Cooper-Hewitt Museum of Decorative Arts & Design)

14 *Machine print*. 1840-50, America; approx. L. 25½″, W. 18″. Blue and red medallions on red patterned background. Inexpensive examples like this were often printed on paper with no ground color. (Courtesy Cooper-Hewitt Museum of Decorative Arts & Design: Illustrated)

15 *Block print, "Pimpernel,"* designed by William Morris in 1876. Reprinted in 1934, England; approx. L. 27″, W. 22½″. Morris's papers represent a continuation of the fine craftsmanship of block printing. The pimpernel design illustrates Morris's dictum that wall-

Machine print. 1840-50, America; approx. L. 25½″, W. 18″.

paper patterns should mask the sequence of repeats. Light green flowers on a background of yellow, blue, and green foliage. (Courtesy Cooper-Hewitt Museum of Decorative Arts & Design)

16 *Block print, covering wooden box.* Nineteenth century, America; approx. L. 8½″, W. 5″. Brown and beige floral pattern on a brown background. (HM)

17 *Block print, covering cardboard bandbox,* (box) "Unidentified Chapel and Buildings," (lid) "Quadriga Filled with Flowers," (label) B. F. Moore. 1830-50, Providence, Rhode Island; approx. L. 17″, W. 13½″, H. 11″. By the 1820s and 30s, the production of printed papers for bandbox coverings was an important branch of American wallpaper manufacture. (WM)

18 *Block print, covering cardboard box in the shape of a comb,* Joseph L. Freeman. Nineteenth century, New Bedford, Massachusetts; approx. L. 8″, W. 4″, H. 7½″. Labeled. Red roses on a brown background. (WM)

19 *Block print.* Eighteenth century, Europe; W. 20″. An elaborate gold floral pattern on blue ground bordered with a Greek key motif covers this paper from the Cadwalader mansion in Philadelphia. (Courtesy A. L. Diament & Company: Displayed in shop front)

20 *Block print, strips 1 and 2 of scenic paper, "Vues de l'Amerique du Nord."* Modern reprinting from original blocks made in 1834, France; W. 18½″. Couples strolling beside a river enjoy a pastoral scene. The thirty-two strips of paper were printed by 1,674 blocks. (Courtesy A. L. Diament & Company: Displayed in shop front)

21 *Block print, covering cardboard bandbox.* About 1830, France; L. 8″, W. 5½″, H. 3⅜″. There is a white and gold leaf and dot pattern on the box. The lid is covered with a romantic scene of children in a gondola, surrounded by a cartouche. (HM: Displayed in shop front)

22 *Block print, covering cardboard bandbox.* About 1840, America; L. 17″, W. 12½″, H. 4″. This commemorative scene on a blue background with orange flowers celebrates William Henry Harrison. (WM: Displayed in shop front)

23 *Block print, covering cardboard bandbox.* Nineteenth century, America; Diam. 10″, H. 4″. A white background with red and blue roses. (HM: Displayed in shop front)

24 *Block print, covering cardboard bandbox.* About 1840, America; L. 17″, W. 12½″, H. 4″. A blue background with orange flowers. (HM: Displayed in shop front)

25 *The wood block.* (Photograph courtesy A. L. Diament & Company)

26 *Preparing the ground.* (Photograph courtesy A. L. Diament & Company)

27 *The color tub.* (Photograph courtesy A. L. Diament & Company)

28 *Hand printing with blocks.* (Photograph courtesy of A. L. Diament & Company)

29 *Laying the Ground.* From *Artistic Wall Papers Designed and Manufactured by Fr. Beck & Co.* (New York: New York and Brooklyn Publishing Co., 1881).

30 *The Twelve-Color Printing Machine.* From *Artistic Wall Papers Designed and Manufactured by Fr. Beck & Co.* (New York: New York and Brooklyn Publishing Co., 1881). (Illustrated)

31 *Flocking.* From *Artistic Wall Papers Designed and Manufactured by Fr. Beck & Co.* (New York: New York and Brooklyn Publishing Co., 1881).

32 *Winding into Rolls.* From *Artistic Wall Papers Designed and Manufactured by Fr. Beck & Co.* (New York: New York and Brooklyn Publishing Co., 1881).

III. Guns: Hand and Machine Made

In the eighteenth century, the gunsmith was master of many skills. As a worker in iron, the gunsmith first had to forge the rifle barrel. Beginning with a rough piece of iron, he hammered it flat and beveled its edges. After heating, the iron was rounded over a rod or mandrel on the gunsmith's anvil, called the swedge block. The metal was then welded together by its own heat under the blows of the hammer (21, illustrated). Cutting, careful hammering, and reaming made the inside of the barrel perfectly smooth. The smith then rifled or cut spiral grooves on the inside of the barrel to ensure accurate firing. As a worker in wood, the gunsmith sawed out a rough pattern that he shaped to accommodate the metal parts of the gun. Each stock was made to suit the taste and anatomy of the individual customer.

Nineteenth-century mass production and new machinery introduced radical changes into gun making. Armories could now manufacture more and cheaper weapons. While the gunsmith had been a craftsman who worked at his own discretion and infused his wares with personal touches, the new techniques of production imposed new values (11, 12, 13, illustrated). In time, factory manufacture demanded conformity to the pace and style of the machine. Although workers developed different skills and abilities in this new technology, they were to a greater degree subservient to machines.

Machines were applied to each of the different processes for producing the metal parts of the gun. Notably, machines drilled barrels from a solid iron rod, thus ending the danger of barrels splitting at hand-forged seams. Human skills and manual operations still played a part in production, but they were relegated to a secondary role. Attention focused not on the craftsman but on the armory.

One important change was the use of the Blanchard tracing machine to turn gun stocks (15, illustrated). With speed and accuracy it reproduced gun stocks by tracing the irregular shape of a master pattern and transferring the design to a rough piece of wood (17, illustrated). Other machines cut beds or depressions in the stock to receive the barrel, lock, butt-plate, sideplates, and trigger guard. By 1854 all operations could be performed on one gun stock in approximately twenty-two minutes, a great saving in time over hand processes.

5 *Blanchard pistol-grip lathe* with working parts labeled. Late nineteenth century, America; L. 43″, W. 25″, H. 37½″.

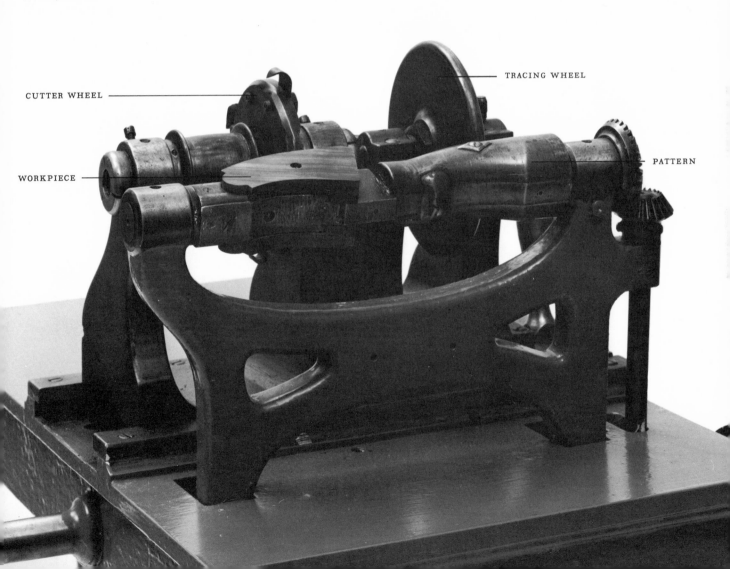

CUTTER WHEEL

TRACING WHEEL

WORKPIECE

PATTERN

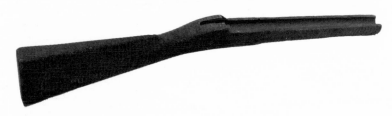

17 *Blanchard lathe-turned rifle stock.* About 1870, Springfield, Massachusetts; L. 31″.

1 *Octagonal barrel.* Eighteenth century, America; L. 44½″, Diam. ¾″. In this example the gunsmith did not lavish work or detail on unexposed parts of the gun, in this case the underside of the barrel. (Courtesy Reaves F. Goehring, Jr.)

2 *Octagonal and round barrel.* Eighteenth century, America; L. 39¾″, Diam. ¾″. An illustration of a single craftman's or purchaser's preference for individual design. (Courtesy Reaves F. Goehring, Jr.)

3 *Octagonal barrel forgings.* Modern reproduction, America; L. 14″, Diam. ¾″; L. 8″, Diam. 1″. Unfinished examples showing visible hammer marks and seams. (Courtesy Messrs. Goehring and Gessler)

4 *Gunsmith's anvil,* called a swedge block or buffalo head. Nineteenth century, America; H. 11¼″, W. 13½″, D. 4½″. (Courtesy Pennsylvania Farm Museum of Landis Valley)

5 *Armorer's long bit.* Eighteenth century, America; L. 53″. For reaming the rifle bore. (Courtesy Reaves F. Goehring, Jr.)

6 *Barrel clamp* from a rifling bench. Eighteenth century, America; H. 9″, W. 5½″. (Courtesy Reaves F. Goehring, Jr.)

7 *Rough-cast trigger guard.* Modern reproduction, America; L. 7¾″, H. 1½″. (Courtesy Reaves F. Goehring, Jr.)

8 *Wrap-out pattern for casting trigger guards.* Modern reproduction, America; H. 5½″, W. 9¾″. (Courtesy Reaves F. Goehring, Jr.)

9 *Narrow-framed pit saw.* Nineteenth century, America; L. 58½″, W. 18½″. This type of saw was occasionally used by gunsmiths for sawing their own planks for rifle stocks. (Courtesy Reaves F. Goehring, Jr.)

21 *Forging a rifle barrel on a gunsmith's anvil.*

10 *Maple blank for rifle stock.* America; L. 59¾". (Courtesy Pennsylvania Farm Museum of Landis Valley)

11 *Pennsylvania long rifle,* N. Beyer. About 1790, Annville, Pennsylvania; L. 50¾". Marked. A notable example of the Pennsylvania rifle, the epitome of eighteenth-century American firearms craftsmanship. (WM: Illustrated)

12 *Manufactured musket,* E. Whitney. 1835, Connecticut; L. 57½". Marked. The product of a partially successful effort to apply early techniques of mass production and interchangeable parts manufacture. (Courtesy Dr. Harry J. Repman: Illustrated)

13 *Trap-door rifle,* Springfield armory. 1881, Springfield, Massachusets; L. 51¾". Marked. This armory-made rifle is a product of a fully mechanized production process. (Courtesy Dr. Harry J. Repman: Illustrated)

14 *Machine-drilled barrel.* About 1860, Springfield, Massachusetts; L. 42", Diam. ¾". (Courtesy Springfield Armory Museum, Inc.)

15 *Blanchard pistol-grip lathe.* Late nineteenth century, America; H. 37½", W. 24¼", D. 39½". This lathe was used for turning pistol grips at the Smith and Wesson factory, Springfield, Massachusetts, until 1964. It is displayed with a target-style pistol grip first patented in 1917. Blanchard's lathe was one of the most important and ingenious American technological innovations. Its tracing principle was applied in the manufacture of all kinds of irregularly shaped objects such as shoe lasts and wheel spokes. (Courtesy American Precision Museum, Inc.: Illustrated)

16 *Unfinished pistol grip.* Nineteenth century, America; L. 4½". This example shows turning marks from a Blanchard lathe. (Courtesy Reaves F. Goehring, Jr.)

17 *Blanchard lathe-turned rifle stock.* About 1870, Springfield, Massachusetts; L. 31". Shows turning marks from Blanchard lathe. (Courtesy Springfield Armory Museum, Inc.: Illustrated)

18 *Rifle stock.* 1842, America; L. 36". An armory-made stock. (Courtesy Reaves F. Goehring, Jr.)

19 *Drop-forged hammers.* Nineteenth century, America; unfiled part with flashing, H. 1¾"; flashing trimmed off, H. 2⅜"; finished part —polished and engraved, H. 2⅜"; three examples for different size guns showing progressive stages of finishing. (Courtesy Reaves F. Goehring, Jr.)

11 *Pennsylvania long rifle,* N. Beyer. About 1790, Annville, Pennsylvania; L. 50¾″.

12 *Manufactured musket,* E. Whitney. 1835, Connecticut; L. 57½″.

13 *Trap-door rifle,* Springfield armory. 1880, Springfield, Massachusetts; L. 51¾″.

20 *Machine-made hammers and lock plates.* About 1860, Springfield, Massachusetts; L. 5¾″; L. 5¾″; L. 5½″. (Courtesy Springfield Armory Museum, Inc.)

21 *Forging a rifle barrel on a gunsmith's anvil.* Still photograph from filmstrip "The Gunsmith." (Courtesy Colonial Williamsburg, Inc.: Illustrated)

22 *Casting trigger guards.* Still photograph from filmstrip "The Gunsmith." (Courtesy Colonial Williamsburg, Inc.)

23 *Sawing a rifle stock with a pit saw.* Still photograph from filmstrip "The Gunsmith." (Courtesy Colonial Williamsburg, Inc.)

24 *Rifling a barrel.* Still photograph from filmstrip "The Gunsmith." (Courtesy Colonial Williamsburg, Inc.)

25 *Manufacture of firearms at E. Remington & Sons armory,* Ilion, New York. From *Scientific American,* n. ser. 45, no. 10 (Sept. 3, 1881): cover.

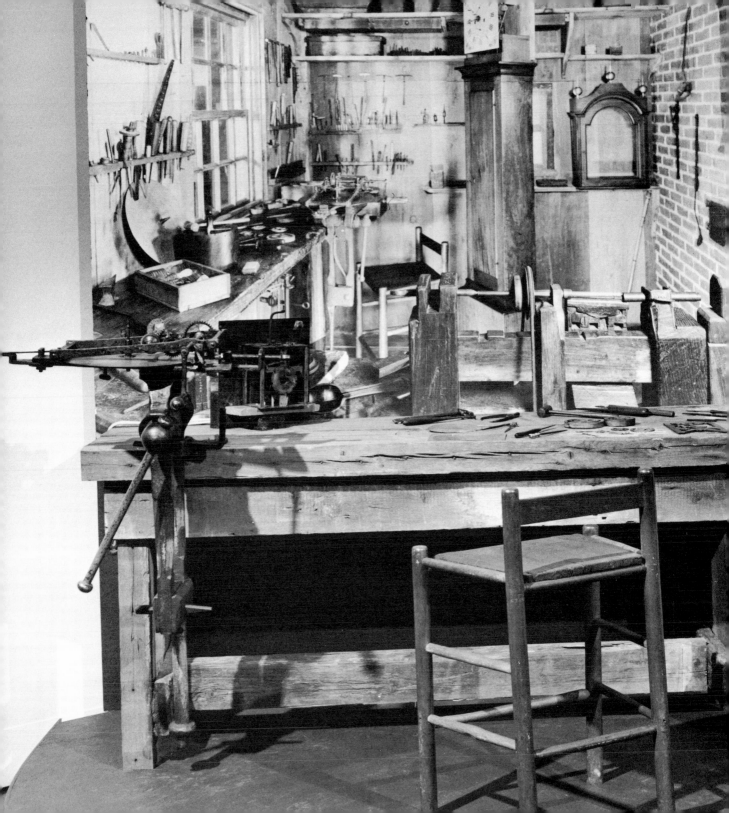

IV. Clocks: Handcrafted and Mass-produced

The eighteenth-century clockmaker was a craftsman who worked in both wood and metal. He used simple hand tools such as saws, files, hammers, and some small hand machines, notably the wheel-cutting engine and the clock lathe (20, illustrated). Clock wheels or gears were made of brass that had been cast in sand and then hand finished. Teeth were cut in the blank gears, using the wheel-cutting engine, and then filed smooth. Clock cases were also made entirely by hand but often by a cabinetmaker. Hand manufacture of a tall clock could take several months. The cost of the labor combined with the scarcity of brass made these clocks beyond the means of all but the well-to-do.

The high cost of brass forced clockmakers to seek a less expensive material. Wooden clockworks were made in America beginning in the 1790s. Gideon Roberts of Bristol, Connecticut, developed the process of making wooden works in lots of like parts. Clockmaking in Connecticut was the first industry to gain commercial success through mass production, a system of manufacture that Eli Terry was largely responsible for initiating. In 1809 he used machinery to produce interchangeable parts for four thousand wooden tall clock movements. Of equal importance was Terry's invention of the one-day shelf clock patented in 1816 (16, 17, illustrated). In following years, competition led to many modifications of movements and cases. Around 1840 the advent of the inexpensive one-day brass movement for clocks ended the popularity of the wooden movement shelf clock.

When blanking or stamping machinery for shearing circular blanks from rolled sheet brass was developed in the 1830s, brass wheels could be made so rapidly that each clock cost less than fifty cents to manufacture. Using a stamping machine or drop hammer, three men could make the wheels for five hundred clocks in a day by stamping out the blanks from sheet brass and then cutting the gears.

Dominy clock shop with original chair, hand tools, wheel-cutting engine, and reconstructed bench in the foreground.

By 1840 Charles Kirk and Joseph Ives perfected an inexpensive clock driven by a coiled brass spring instead of weights. To accommodate and to take advantage of the new, more compact spring movements, a line of smaller clock-case designs was developed, such as the gothic or steeple clocks produced by Chauncey Jerome and his competitors (18, 19, illustrated). By 1850 clock manufacturers like Jerome were using steam-powered machinery, although many production steps were still hand done. It was the beginning of a period of simple factory technology in the American clock industry.

1-12 *Clockmakers' tools used by the Dominy family.* Eighteenth and nineteenth centuries, East Hampton, Long Island. (WM, funds for purchase, gift of Henry Belin du Pont and Crestlea Foundation)

1 *Wheel-cutting engine* (iron), used for cutting gears on clock wheels; L. 27½ ″, W. 16⅝ ″.

2 *Exercise plates and templates* (silver, copper, brass), illustrating the use of scrap metal for practicing engraving; L. 7½ ″, W. 5⅛ ″; L. 5⅜ ″, W. 5⅝ ″.

3 *Pattern and templates for clock wheels* (wood, brass); pattern: Diam. 4⅛ ″; templates: Diams. 3¼ ″; 1¹³⁄₁₆″; 2½ ″; 2⅛ ″.

4 *Plate pattern* (brass), used to design the mounting plate for the clockworks; L. 7¹¹⁄₁₆″, W. 5¼ ″.

5 *Files* (steel, wood), used to finish the metal parts; L. 8⅝ ″; L. 7¾ ″; L. 7″; L. 8⅜ ″.

6 *Lathe tools* (wood, steel), used with the lathe to fashion turned parts; L. 8⅞ ″; L. 10⅛ ″.

7 *Calipers* (iron), used for the precise measurement of metal parts; L. 4⅜ ″.

8 *Dividers* (brass, steel), used to scribe and mark circular outlines for cutting; L. 5⅞ ″.

9 *Hammers* (wood, steel), used, among other things, to form and fashion the iron parts; L. 9³⁄₁₆″; L. 8¹³⁄₁₆″.

10 *Mallet* (leather, wood), used to form soft metals such as brass and silver; L. 8¾ ″.

11 *Frame saw* (iron, steel), used to rough cut small metal parts; L. 7⁵⁄₁₆″.

12 *Hour- and minute-hand templates* (brass, copper), used as guides in making the metal hands; L. 2¹³⁄₁₆″; L. 3⁷⁄₁₆″; L. 4⅛ ″.

13 *Tall clock,* Daniel Burnap. 1785-90, East Windsor, Connecticut; H. 89″, W. 18″, D. 10″. Maker's name engraved on clockface. (WM)

14 *Tall clock movement* (wood). About 1810, Connecticut; H. 11¼ ″, W. 12″, D. 4½ ″. A movement for a one-day tall clock using gears made of cherry, plates of quarter sawn oak, and tiny pinions and shafts of mountain laurel. The various parts were mass-produced. (Courtesy Edward F. LaFond, Jr.)

9 *Clock movement* (brass), E. Ingraham & Co. About 1800, Bristol, Connecticut; H. 4¾ ″.

16-17 *Pillar and scroll clock with wooden works,* Eli Terry. About 1820, Plymouth, Connecticut; H. 31¾″. Shown with wooden works for pillar and scroll clock, Eli Terry. About 1820, Plymouth, Connecticut; H. 9″.

18 *Sharp gothic (steeple) clock with brass clockworks,* Chauncey Jerome. About 1850, Connecticut; H. 22″.

15 *Clock movement* (brass). About 1765, England; H. 10¼″, W. 5¾″, D. 6″. This movement, made for a small wall clock, represents good English country hand workmanship, comparable to American work. A thirty-hour movement like this required less brass and was therefore less expensive than an eight-day movement. (Courtesy John H. Hill)

16 *Pillar and scroll clock with wooden works,* Eli Terry. About 1820, Plymouth, Connecticut; H. 31¾″, W. 17¾″, D. 4½″. Paper label. Attractive pillar and scroll cases played an important part in the successful introduction of inexpensive shelf clocks. (HM: Illustrated)

17 *Wooden works for pillar and scroll clock,* Eli Terry. About 1820, Plymouth, Connecticut; H. 9″, W. 6½″, D. 2½″. Eli Terry's 1816 patent for thirty-hour brass and wooden clocks stated "this improvement consists in the following properties. Vis: In being smaller, handsomer, less cumbersome, cheaper including the case, easier moved from one room to another, and cheaper transported, and in having the weights in sight so that there is no danger of letting it run down and stop." (Courtesy John H. Hill: Illustrated)

18 *Sharp gothic (steeple) clock with brass clockworks,* Chauncey Jerome. About 1850, Connecticut; H. 22″, W. 11¼″, D. 4½″. (Courtesy Edward F. LaFond, Jr.: Illustrated)

19 *Clock movement* (brass), E. Ingraham & Co. About 1880, Bristol, Connecticut; H. 4¾″, W. 4″, D. 1½″. Stamped. Note the precision of the stamped brass parts in this late nineteenth-century mass-produced movement made to fit a small case. The Chauncey Jerome clock (18) used this type of clockworks. (Courtesy John H. Hill: Illustrated)

20 *Photo mural of Dominy clock shop* with original chair, hand tools, wheel-cutting engine, and reconstructed bench in the foreground. The original clock shop was used by the Dominy craftsmen of East Hampton, Long Island, during the eighteenth and nineteenth centuries. It is now installed at the Winterthur Museum. (Illustrated)

21 *Drawing of power punch press* similar to presses used for blanking out clockwheels from sheet brass. From James G. Benton, *The Fabrication of Small Arms for The U.S. Service,* Ordnance Memoranda 22 (1878; reprint ed., Glendale, N.Y.: Benchmark Publishing Co., 1970).

V. Iron Casting: Process and Products

Cast iron was a traditional material used for domestic utensils and industrial and agricultural equipment. Loam casting, an early process used for both iron and bronze, was superseded in the first half of the nineteenth century by two basic methods: the older method was flat-bed casting, the newer method was flask casting (1-11, illustrated). Loam casting was costly because the molds took much time to make and could be used only once. Both the nineteenth-century processes used sand molds, which took less time to make and were often reuseable.

In flat-bed casting the workmen ladled molten iron from a tap in the furnace directly into molds created by patterns impressed in the sand floor of the ironworks. Flat-bed casting produced only flat, thick pieces such as stove plates, and the decoration on flat-bed cast objects tended to be coarse and imprecise.

In flask casting molten metal was ladled into molds of dry sand packed in three-part wooden boxes, called flasks (12, illustrated). The mold was created by a pattern that was removed before casting. Flask casting produced a variety of flat or curved objects such as pots (17, 18, illustrated) and curved stove plates. And because the use of highly cohesive sand allowed the molding of precise details, flask-cast plates could be thin and show fine detail (20, illustrated).

Charcoal iron, iron made with charcoal as fuel in the smelting process, was used for most American cast-iron objects until the 1850s. After that time the increased use of coke as a fuel in combination with improved casting methods using more fluid iron heated to higher temperatures resulted in thinner, lighter pots and even finer decorative designs.

1 *Tools and reconstructed bench used in flask casting,* including flask, rammer, bellows, ladle, ladle carrier, riddle, and pattern. 1875-1970, America.

1-11 *Tools and reconstruction of bench used in flask casting.* 1875-1970, America. (Tools, courtesy Hopewell Village National Historical Site: Illustrated)

1 *Ladle.* Diam. 8¼″.

2 *Laddle carrier* used to transport molten metal. L. 47″.

3 *Flask, in two parts.* L. 19½″, W. 14¾″, H. 10¼″.

4 *Follow boards,* for holding the pattern while the sand was packed. L. 19½″, W. 14¾″.

5 *Pattern for stove plate* (originally in wood, reproduced here in aluminum), John I. Hess. About 1850, Philadelphia; H. 15″, W. 10″.

6 *Riddle,* sifted sand for the mold. Diam. 15½″.

7 *Rammer,* used to pack sand around the pattern. L. 14½″.

8 *Bellows,* for blowing away loose sand. L. 19″, W. 9½″.

9 *Strike,* to cut away surplus sand. L. 28¾″.

10 *Steel wedge,* to make an opening or gate for molten metal to enter the flask. L. 4″, W. 3¼″.

11 *Clamps,* to fasten the parts of the flask together. L. 12″, W. ¾″.

12 *Pattern for a bearing plate* (wood). H. 16″. (HM: Illustrated)

13 *Cooking pot* (bronze). 1500-1700, Europe; H. 8″, Diam. 7″. Loam cast. (Courtesy Pennsylvania Historical & Museum Commission)

12 *Flask with wooden pattern* for a bearing plate and rammer.

7   *Cooking pot* (iron). About 1800,
    America; H. 9″, Diam. 10″.

8   *Cooking pot* (iron). About 1870,
    America; H. 10½″, Diam. 13″.

14 *Stove plate* (iron), Valentine Eckert, Sally Ann Furnace. About 1790, Pennsylvania; H. 35½", W. 26". Flat-bed cast. Marked. Eagle, shield, and banner inscribed: "E PLURIBUS/UNUM." (Courtesy Pennsylvania Historical & Museum Commission)

15 *Stove plate* (iron), Pine Grove Furnace. About 1800, Pennsylvania; H. 25", W. 17½". Flat-bed cast. Marked. Pelican standing on one foot in frame of C-scrolls. (Courtesy Pennsylvania Historical & Museum Commission)

16 *Cooking pot* (iron). About 1750, America; H. 6¾", Diam. 6½". Flask cast. (Courtesy Pennsylvania Historical & Museum Commission)

17 *Cooking pot* (iron). About 1800, America; H. 9", Diam. 10". Flask cast. (Courtesy Pennsylvania Historical & Museum Commission: Illustrated)

18 *Cooking pot* (iron). About 1870, America; H. 10½", Diam. 13". Flask cast. Legs have disappeared and been replaced by a rim, which allowed the pot to sit on top of a wood stove. (Courtesy Pennsylvania Historical & Museum Commission: Illustrated)

19 *Stove plate* (iron), D. & S. Hughes Furnace. About 1813, Pennsylvania; H. 35", W. 25". Flask cast. Neoclassical decoration and a ship. Inscribed: "Don't Give Up the Ship." (Courtesy Pennsylvania Historical & Museum Commission)

20 *End plate of fire frame* (iron). About 1820, America; H. 31", W. 10½". Flask cast. (Courtesy Pennsylvania Historical & Museum Commission: Illustrated)

End plate of fire frame (iron). About 1820, America; H. 31", W. 10½".

VI. Textile Printing: By Hand and By Machine

During the seventeenth century, Indian printed fabrics arriving in England spawned new interest in printed textiles. Printed cloth added color and design to furnishings and wardrobes, and the popularity of Indian cottons provided incentive for increased production and more efficient techniques in the developing British textile-printing industry.

British printers were imitating Indian block-printed fabrics by 1680. Despite opposition from weavers who lobbied against use of domestic or imported calicoes, printers produced over one million yards yearly by the mid-eighteenth century. Although American firms were hard pressed to compete with the quantities of English textiles imported, by the Revolutionary period a few fine printers were established. John Hewson, Thomas Bedwell, and John Walters, all of Philadelphia, left documented examples of their work.

Block printing, a relief process, produced cloth with rich, pure colors and striking designs, free from excessive detail. In this process the printing table and blocks were the printer's two major tools (22, illustrated). The table's thick, blanket-covered top provided a firm but resilient work surface for the hand-carved wooden blocks with raised designs. Some early blocks had pitch pins at the edges that printed guide dots on the fabric, insuring crisp, matched, well-registered patterns. Printing was precise and time-consuming, requiring different blocks and separate printings for each color. The design was stamped on the fabric with mordants (color-fixing chemicals). Each color required a different mordant and a separate printing with different blocks. The printer's skill insured correct registry, or placement, of the overlapping patterns and colors of the design. Shades of red, purple, brown, and black appeared after the fabric was immersed in a vegetable madder dye. The printer added blue and yellow by hand (1, illustrated). Printing with hand blocks has continued

Block print (cotton). 1775-90, England; L. 71″, W. 36″.

to the present (17, illustrated). Throughout the nineteenth century, designs changed with emerging tastes, and old motifs received new interpretations.

Engraved copperplates, long employed to print paper, were used on fabrics after 1750. This intaglio printing process, using incised lines instead of raised surfaces, required a hand-operated printing press. Designs were usually limited to one color but this process allowed large repeats and produced the fine lines and subtle shadings necessary for pictorial prints (4, illustrated). The expense of engraving plates and the continuous demand for new designs caused a decline in the standard of copperplate engraving after 1800. The process did not survive long past the first quarter of the nineteenth century.

The slowness and expense of hand-printing processes coupled with a growing demand for printed textiles favored the adoption of roller printing. The first successful cylinder-printing machine, patented in 1783 by Thomas Bell, a Scotsman, began the rapid, inexpensive production of printed cloth that dramatically changed the industry and its market. In the 1830s, one machine operated by a man and a boy produced as much as two hundred hand workers.

The process of roller printing has remained largely unchanged. Engraved copper rollers transferred dyestuff to fabric just as copperplates did, but the rollers turned continuously and were mechanically inked and cleaned at every turn (27, illustrated). A color-furnishing roller transferred the coloring agent from a trough to the engraved copper cylinder that printed the cloth. Other parts of the cylinder-printing machine removed excess dye, pressed the fabric against the engraved roller, and caught dust and lint. To produce multicolor patterns, printers used a variety of techniques. They added more engraved rollers, one for each color, to the press; they used wooden relief surface rollers, which printed as wood blocks did, to apply flat color; or they completed the pattern, begun on the roller press, with hand blocks. A multiple-color machine required the same basic roller arrangement for each color.

Craftsmen carefully hand-engraved the earliest rollers, but the introduction of the mill and die simplified the process and reduced the cost. The die, a small cylinder of soft steel, was first engraved with one repeat of the design and then hardened. The die created the pattern in relief on a large cylinder of softened

17 *Textile printing blocks* (wood).
About 1790-1820, Vermont; flower
sprig: L. 5"; rosette:
Diam. 2⅝₁₆"; vase of flowers:
H. 4¼"; leaf: L. 4⁹⁄₁₆".

steel—the mill—as the two were pressed together. The mill, once tempered, was successively pressed around the copper roller, engraving the design on it in intaglio (25, illustrated). The process was frequently used for small-scale background patterns (12, illustrated).

After 1835 the pantograph, a mechanical copying machine, further simplified the engraving process. A diamond-pointed needle attached to the pantograph traced the design through an acid-resistant varnish covering the copper cylinder. Immersion in acid then etched the design into the copper.

The roller press could and did produce the same general type of patterns as hand methods—both the flat color areas of the wood block and the fine, intricate lines of the copperplate. But delicate, detailed roller-printed patterns were characteristically different, although equally appealing, from block-printed designs. Repeat areas in roller prints, determined by the diameter of the roller, were also necessarily shorter than in hand-printed examples.

Early roller prints reflected the styles of popular block prints. By the late eighteenth century, the wall paintings discovered earlier at Pompeii had inspired new designs and colors. The "drab style" followed development of a bright, colorfast yellow dye that produced shades of yellow, olive green, and brown with different mordants. Printers seldom attempted more than one or two colors, and designs consciously avoided the problems of registry. Early roller prints were used frequently as furniture fabrics and often adapted patterns from contemporary wallpapers. By 1825 registry had become more accurate and the patterns more daring and numerous, but heavy outlines and dark backgrounds still hid uncertain edges. The introduction of mineral dyes produced harsh unnatural colors that replaced the harmony of the earlier vegetable dyes. Both registry and engraving had been perfected by 1835. Later in the century fads often followed the introduction of new dyes, and a succession of revival styles produced a parade of new designs.

Demand for new patterns and the significant expense of engraving copper rollers led to cost cutting that encouraged inferior design and resulted in an early output of cheap, poorly printed fabrics. Nevertheless American manufacturers produced examples of notable quality and competed successfully with British imports by the mid-1800s. Roller prints, even more than hand-printed goods, introduced color and pattern cheaply and conveniently in clothing and home furnishings.

Machine for engraving the cylinders.

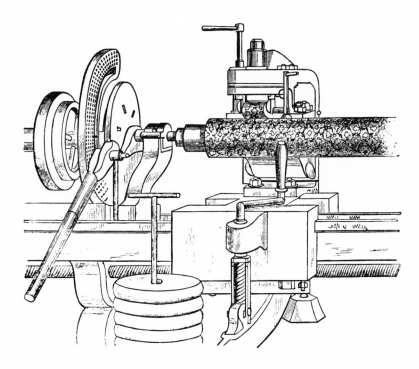

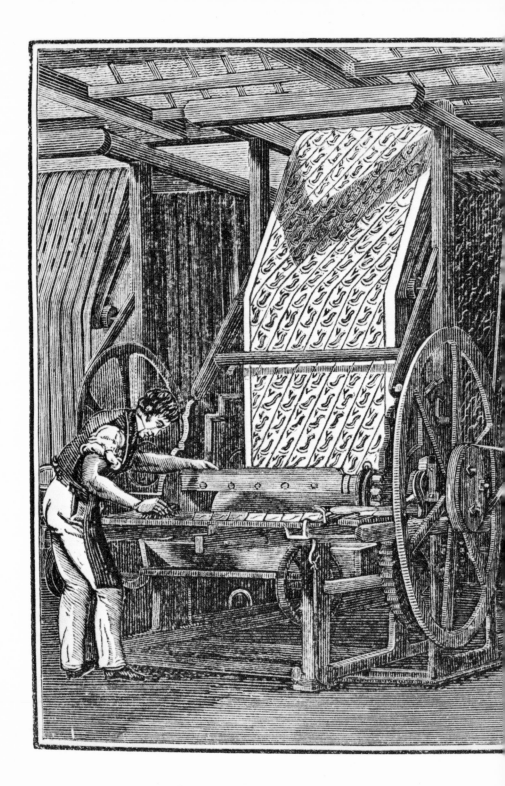

27 *Calico printing,* approximately
1835.

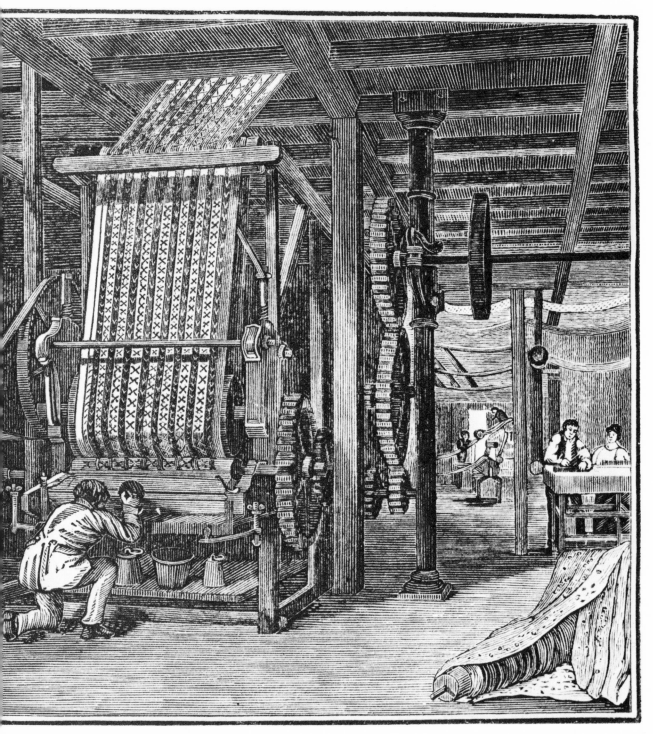

1 *Block print* (cotton). 1775-90, England; L. 71″, W. 36″. The flower motif with cock and hen, in shades of red, green, and brown, exhibits Chinese and Indian influences. Flat patterns, without the illusion of depth, suitable for wallpaper as well as textiles, were favored in this period. (WM: Illustrated)

2 *Block print* (linen), signed by Bedwell and Walters. 1775-76, Philadelphia; L. 7″, W. 12⅞″. This fabric, printed in red and brown, with yellow and blue added in pencil, compares in quality to English work of this date. (WM)

3 *Block print* (cotton). About 1815, England; L. 28″, W. 20″. The pheasant and plum tree motif, printed in red, brown, and black, with yellow and blue added, enjoyed continued popularity. Later roller prints resemble this pattern. (WM)

4 *Copperplate print* (cotton and linen). About 1785, England; L. 37″, W. 31″. "America Presenting at the Altar of Liberty Medallions of Her Illustrious Sons," was based on engravings by Pierre Eugene du Simitière, a Swiss emigrant living in Philadelphia. (WM: Illustrated)

5 *Roller print* (cotton). About 1835, England; L. 21″, W. 23½″. The pheasant and plum tree pattern, printed in red and black, with yellow and blue added, on a brown blotch background, repeats the design of an earlier block print but with a shorter repeat due to the machine printing process (compare to 3). (WM)

6 *Roller print* (cotton). About 1815, England; L. 19½″, W. 23″. A blue pillar print with fruit and squirrel on a white background imitates monochrome copperplate prints. (WM)

7 *Roller print* (cotton). 1807-08, England; L. 12″, W. 22″. The red shade in the design of snowdrops on a dotted and honeycomb background was probably applied with a roller. Yellow was added by hand block or surface roller. (WM, gift of Victoria & Albert Museum)

8 *Roller print* (cotton). 1809-10, England; L. 7″, W. 24″. Yellow flowers and brown leaves were printed on a leafy, shaded background. (WM)

9a *Roller print* (cotton). About 1815, England; L. 12″, W. 17″. The discharge method, in use by 1800, produced white areas in this furniture fabric, when a bleaching agent was printed on a background dyed with blue indigo. The green shade was overprinted. The pattern is similar to the wallpaper sample that Robert Peel, British textile printer, recommended as a source for a textile design. (WM, gift of Victoria & Albert Museum)

9b   *Block print* (wallpaper). 1812, England; L. 8¼″, W. 6⅝″. Wallpaper printed in white and pink on orange ground. On the reverse, Robert Peel (1750-1830), a partner in the calico-printing firm of Haworth, Peel, and Yates in Lancashire, wrote "I think two or three Furniture patts. may be drawn from this Paper." (WM Libraries)

10   *Roller print* (cotton). About 1830, England or America; L. 14″, W. 26″. Rollers applied red and black to a brown blotch background in this floral print. Yellow was added and overprinting produced the green. (WM, gift of Mrs. Reginald P. Rose)

11   *Roller print* (cotton). 1830-34, England; L. 19″, W. 26″. Audubon's *Birds of America* provided accurate models for this pink and yellow design on blue ground, one of a series, but the foliage was invented by the copperplate engraver. (WM, gift of Victoria & Albert Museum)

12   *Roller print* (cotton). About 1830, England; L. 15½″, W. 18⅝″. A floral pattern of rose, brown, green, and white covers a stippled brown and white background. The roller engraving is attributed to Joseph Lockett, who provided rollers to many English printers and popularized the techniques of etching a design through acid-resistant varnish. The heavy dark lines are characteristic of early machine-printed textiles. They were deliberately introduced in the pattern to hide poor registration. (HM: Illustrated)

13   *Roller print* (cotton). About 1834, England; L. 23½″, W. 17½″. This pattern of anemones and peonies printed in pink, tan, and solid green on a beige background was probably produced in Lancashire. (WM, gift of Victoria & Albert Museum)

14   *Roller print* (cotton), Maqueston and Company. 1850-60, America; L. 11″, W. 24″. A precise printing of small-scale flowers on a finely woven fabric with brown, red, blue, yellow, and green was applied by roller with a shading of blue dots. Manufacturer's printed paper label pasted to fabric. (WM)

15 *Roller print* (cotton). About 1837, England; L. 23¼″, W. 18½″. A floral design with red, purple, black, blue, and yellow applied by roller to a tan background. (WM, gift of Victoria & Albert Museum)

16 *Roller print* (cotton). 1835-45, attributed to Globe Print Works, Fall River, Massachusetts, or Eagle Printing Company, Belleville, New Jersey; approx. L. 23″, W. 35⅜″. Floral design, roller printed in brown, rose, green, and purple on chintz with manufacturer's printed paper label. (Courtesy Esther Schwartz)

17 *Textile printing blocks* (wood). About 1790-1820, Vermont; flower sprig: L. 5″; rosette: Diam. 2⁵⁄₁₆″; vase of flowers: H. 4¼″; leaf: L. 4⁹⁄₁₆″. These four small printing blocks may have been used for a small-scale design or for adding detail to a larger design. (WM: Illustrated)

18 *Patent model of roller-printing machine* with reconstructed mock-up of printing rollers. 1838, Pawtucket, Massachusetts; L. 17″, W. 15″, H. 19″. Alden Sibley of Pawtucket applied for a patent on this arrangement of gears linking the furnishing roller and the printing roller, and on this mechanism for adjusting the position of the color box. (Courtesy National Museum of History and Technology)

19 *Die,* Pacific Mills. About 1920, Lawrence, Massachusetts; L. 4½″, Diam. ⅜″. (Courtesy National Museum of History and Technology)

20 *Mill made from die,* Pacific Mills. About 1880, Lawrence, Massachusetts; L. 5″, Diam. 1¼″. (Courtesy National Museum of History and Technology)

21 *Printing roller* (copper), Pacific Mills. About 1880, Lawrence, Massachusetts; L. 31¾″, Diam. 3¾″. (Courtesy National Museum of History and Technology)

22 *Printing table with blocks and hand-printed fabric,* constructed for this exhibit to demonstrate printing by hand. (Illustrated)

23 *Calico printer's trade card,* seventeenth century. From Florence H. Pettit, *America's Printed and Painted Fabrics, 1600-1900* (New York: Hastings House, 1970), opposite p. 19.

4 *Copperplate print* (cotton and linen). About 1785, England; L. 37″, W. 31″.

12 *Roller print* (cotton). About 1830, England; 15½″, W. 18⅝″.

VII. Glass: Blown and Pressed

Due to difficulties from lack of capital and shortages of raw materials, in 1800 American glass-making houses were still small, handcraft operations. The master craftsman in the glasshouse was the gaffer, or master glassblower. His basic tools were his bench, blowpipe, pontil rod, pucella, and various smaller tools used in manipulating molten glass when it came from the melting pot in the furnace (52, illustrated). Molten glass could be blown into many different shapes (26, illustrated), or it could be formed in molds. Glass blown in full-size molds often served as an inexpensive substitute for the costly cut glass imported from the British Isles and Europe. Many patterns for molded glass imitated cut glass, although the outlines and edges of the molded patterns are less precise than those of cut glass. Aside from utilitarian window glass and bottles, molded and free-blown glass tablewares were the basic products of seventeenth-, eighteenth-, and many nineteenth-century American glasshouses.

In 1825 a combination of protective tariffs and technological breakthroughs strengthened and revolutionized the American glass industry. In that year a Pittsburgh firm, Bakewell and Company, took out the first known patent on a glass-pressing mechanism (54, illustrated), in which a mechanically operated plunger replaced the skills of the glassblower. An object was produced by forcing molten glass into a mold whose cavity was made in the shape of the desired form (33, illustrated). This machine greatly reduced the amount of skilled labor and time necessary to produce tablewares and other popular items. By the 1830s pressing machines had improved to the point where large items could be pressed complete with simple feet and handles in one operation.

At first pressed patterns were made in imitation of English cut glass. Early pieces had poor surface quality, and mold makers developed lacy patterns that camouflaged defects and suited the taste of the decade for heavily decorated surfaces (18, 42, illus-

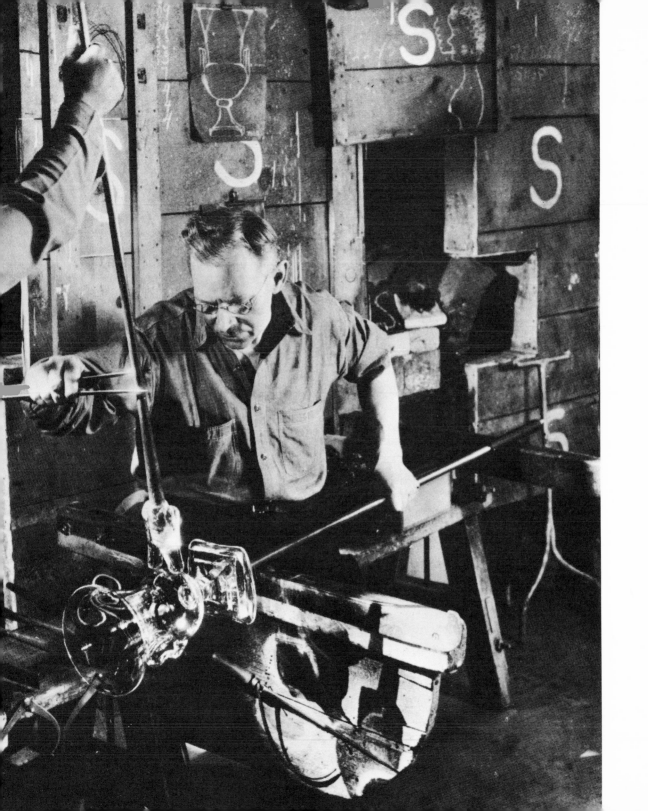

trated). Although the American glass industry led the world in developing pressed glass technology and expanded production to serve a mass market, handwork on luxury glass items continues to this day in the United States.

Glassblower working at bench.
Pressing glass by machine

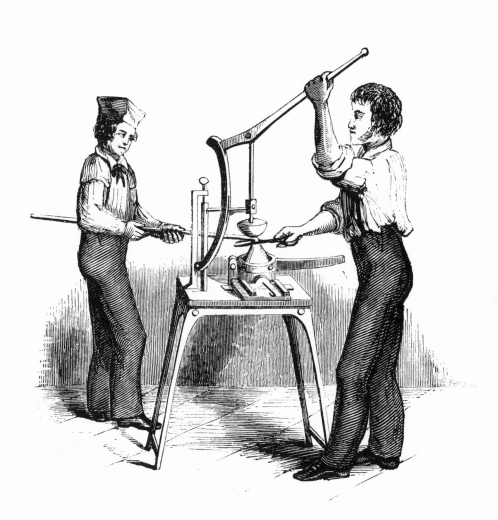

1 *Gaffer's (glassblower's) bench* (wood and iron). 1875-1925, America; H. 25¾", W. 60¼", D. 39¾". At the glassblower's bench, the semimolten gather, or globule of glass, attached to a blowpipe or pontil rod, was fashioned into an object. (WM)

2 *Blowpipe* (iron). 1875-1925, America; L. 53", Diam. 1⅞". The blowpipe, a hollow tube, was the glassblower's basic tool. It was used primarily in forming hollow ware. (WM)

3 *Blocking tool* (wood). 1875-1925, America; L. 10½", W. 4½". The blocking tool, used to make a gather of glass uniform, was the first in a series of shaping tools employed in forming glass objects. (Courtesy The Corning Museum of Glass)

18 *Hinged three-part mold for a bowl* (cast iron). Late nineteenth century, America; L. 10", W. 10", H. 4⅛". The reproduction plastic bowl shown in the foreground illustrates the pattern.

Furniture knobs, Bakewell and Company. 1825-35, Pittsburgh; H. 1 9/16 ", Diam. 2 1/8 ".

4 *Pucella* (steel). 1875-1925, America; L. 14 7/8 ", W. 3 3/8 ". The pucella, a pointed tonglike device, was used in shaping glass objects. (WM)

5 *Trimming shears* (steel, leather, and cloth). 1875-1925, America; L. 11 5/8 ", W. 5". Stamped "Moxer/Alamarge" on each blade. Glass in a semimolten state can be cut with shears to achieve smooth edges. (WM)

6 *Calipers* (iron). 1875-1925, America; L. 11", W. (open) 14". "HK" near the top of one arm. Calipers were used to gauge the dimensions of glass objects. (WM)

7 *Battledore* (carbon and wood). 1875-1925, America; L. 11", W. 2 5/8 ". The battledore, a flat, paddle-shaped piece of wood faced with carbon, was also a shaping tool. (WM)

8 *Spring tool* (sheet metal). 1875-1925, America; L. 10 1/4 ", W. 2 1/4 ". A tonglike spring tool with flat, spatulate ends was used in shaping. (WM)

9 *Marker* (wood, steel, and chalk). 1875-1925, America; L. 12 7/8 ", Diam. 1 3/16 ". The marker was used for placing chalk marks on glass objects during working. (WM)

10 *Necking tool* (iron and rubber). 1875-1925, America; L. 11", W. 3". The necking tool was used to form the neck and neck ring of a bottle. (WM)

11 *Pontil* (or punty) rod (iron). 1875-1925, America; L. 50 3/4 ". After being removed from the blowpipe, a glass object was held on the pontil rod for final shaping and finishing of the rim. (Courtesy The Corning Museum of Glass)

12 *Lipper* (carbon and wood). 1875-1925, America; L. 10 3/4 ". The lipper, a carbon rod attached to a wooden handle, was used to form and flare rims on glass objects. (WM)

13 *Foot former* (steel). 1875-1925, America; L. 10 3/4 ", W. (closed) 4". The foot former helped to flatten and spread a gather of glass into a circular foot. (WM)

14 *Two-part diamond and rib mold* (brass?), New Geneva (Gallatin) Glass Works. About 1810, New Geneva, Pennsylvania; H. 3 3/4 ", W. 2". Molds for glass objects were often made in two or three parts hinged together, so the molded pieces could be removed easily (see cat. no. 31). (Courtesy The Corning Museum of Glass)

15 *Hinged three-part mold for bottle* (brass or iron). About 1840, America; H. 5¼", W. 6½". Inscribed on top "Potomac" and "AFGW," possibly for the American Flint Glass Workers (see cat. no. 28). (Courtesy Charles B. Gardner's Collection)

16 *Vertical dip mold with twenty ribs* (brass or iron), New Geneva (Gallatin) Glass Works. About 1810, New Geneva, Pennsylvania; H. 5¾", Diam. 3½". In dip molding a gather of glass on the blow-pipe was impressed in the mold. The mold was then removed, and when the gather was blown to full size the pattern remained (see cat. no. 32). (Courtesy The Corning Museum of Glass)

17 *Frog mold* (iron). 1900-40, America; H. 3¼", Diam. 7¾". Glass could be cast solid in this mold for making a doorstop in the shape of a frog. (WM)

18 *Hinged three-part mold for a bowl* (cast iron). Late nineteenth century, America; L. 10", W. 10", H. 4⅛". Intaglio pattern with rim mold and plunger. Inscribed on top "AFGWU" for American Flint Glass Workers' Union and "Victor." The plastic bowl shown with the mold illustrates the pattern as it would appear on a bowl cast in this mold. (Courtesy Pennsylvania Historical & Museum Commission: Illustrated)

19 *Three-part mold* (iron). 1900-40, Flemington-Clayton area, New Jersey; Diam. 7", H. 5¾". Molds like this, with an overall pattern of dots, were called "popcorn" molds. (WM)

20 *Vase mold with base and cover plates* (iron). 1900-40, Flemington-Clayton area, New Jersey; top plate: Diam. 8¼"; body: Diam. 10", H. 6½". The interior shape of this mold produces a vase in the form of a six-pointed star ornamented with floral motifs. A plastic cast exhibited with the mold shows how the product of this mold would look. (WM)

21 *Lamp chimney mold* (wood). Nineteenth century, America; H. 18", Diam. 9¾". A gather of glass was blown and rotated in the mold to yield a form without the marks of the mold seams. (WM)

22 *Amethyst-colored flask.* 1765-74, possibly Manheim, Pennsylvania; H. 5½", W. 3⅞". A "Stiegel" type, patterned in a part-size mold. (WM)

23 *Aquamarine-tinted jug.* 1800-50, America; H. 8", Diam. (base) 3¾". Blown glass. (WM)

24 *Lamp chimney*. 1800-50, England or America; H. 13$\frac{15}{16}$″, Diam. 6$\frac{11}{16}$″. Blown. Forms similar to this were also made in molds (see mold 21). (WM)

25 *Tumbler,* attributed to Pittsburgh Glass Works. 1810-20, Pittsburgh, Pennsylvania; H. 3$\frac{3}{8}$″, Diam. (top) 3$\frac{1}{8}$″. Blown, cut, and engraved. An example of an expensive glass piece presented as a gift from the family of Colonel James O'Hara, owner of the Pittsburgh Glass Works, to Victorine du Pont Bauduy and inscribed with her initials. (WM, gift of Mrs. E. du Pont Irving)

26 *Aquamarine-colored compote,* probably Redwood or Redford glass factories, 1830-50, Watertown or Plattsburg, New York; H. 4$\frac{1}{4}$″, Diam. (rim) 8$\frac{5}{8}$″. A free-blown glass bowl with an applied gather of glass shaped into lily pad motifs. (WM: Illustrated)

27 *Tumbler*. 1820-40, probably New England; H. 3$\frac{3}{8}$″, Diam. 2$\frac{1}{2}$″. Blown in a hinged, full-size mold with sunburst and diamond patterns. (WM)

28 *Bottle*. About 1840, America; H. 5$\frac{3}{4}$″, Diam. 2$\frac{3}{4}$″. Blown in bottle mold (see mold 15). (Courtesy Charles B. Gardner's Collection)

29 *Lamp,* New England Glass Company. 1830-40, Cambridge, Massachusetts; H. 10$\frac{3}{4}$″, W. 3$\frac{1}{8}$″. Marked. Pressed base, blown font. (WM)

30 *Green-colored flask*. 1830-41, Keene, New Hampshire; H. 7″, W. 4$\frac{3}{4}$″. Patterned in a full-size, two-part mold. Flasks were often decorated with commemorative designs like this one proclaiming "Success to the Railroad." (WM, gift of Charles van Ravenswaay)

31 *Wine glass*. 1900-10, Mt. Pleasant, Pennsylvania; H. 3$\frac{1}{2}$″. This pattern-molded wine glass from a two-part diamond mold (see mold 14) shows the pattern of the mold in reverse on its inner surfaces. (Courtesy The Corning Museum of Glass)

32 *Sherbet glass*. 1910, Mt. Pleasant, Pennsylvania; H. 4″. Blown molded in a dip mold with twenty vertical ribs (see mold 16). The diffused, imprecise quality of the bowl resulted from blowing the glass after patterning it in the mold. (Courtesy The Corning Museum of Glass)

33 *Furniture knobs,* Bakewell and Company. 1825-35, Pittsburgh, Pennsylvania; H. 1$\frac{9}{16}$″, Diam. 2$\frac{1}{8}$″. Marked "Bakewell/Patent." Pressed glass. John Palmer Bakewell's 1825 patent for pressed glass furniture knobs inaugurated the pressed glass industry in

America. The process was soon applied to forming many different kinds of objects. (WM, gift of Mr. and Mrs. Richard Gould: Illustrated)

34 *Compote,* Boston and Sandwich Glass Company. 1830-40, Sandwich, Massachusetts; H. 5⅝", Diam. 7⅜". An early example of pressed glass incorporating the currently popular Empire style in its elaborate feet. The bowl and feet were pressed separately and joined together by a pad of molten glass. (WM)

35 *Plate,* probably Boston and Sandwich Glass Company. 1830-40, Sandwich, Massachusetts; Diam. 5¼". Lacy peacock-feather and scrolled-eye pattern. (Courtesy The Sandwich Glass Museum)

36 *Plate* (iron). 1830-40, possibly Sandwich, Massachusetts; Diam. 5¼". This iron plate was made in a mold taken from a glass dish with a lacy peacock-feather and scrolled-eye pattern. (Courtesy The Sandwich Glass Museum)

37 *Blue-colored cup plate,* possibly Boston and Sandwich Glass Company. 1820-40, Sandwich, Massachusetts; Diam. 3⁹⁄₁₆". Pressed glass. Cup plates were made by the thousands with commemorative, patriotic, or historical motifs like this bust of Henry Clay. (WM, gift of Mrs. Alfred C. Harrison)

26 *Aquamarine-colored compote,* probably Redwood or Redford glass factories. 1830-50, Watertown or Plattsburg, New York; H. 4¼", Diam. (rim) 8⅝".

38 *Amethyst-colored salt boat,* Stourbridge Flint Glass Works (Robinson and Son). 1829-30, Pittsburgh, Pennsylvania; L. 3½″, W. 1⅞″, H. 1½″. Pressed glass. Salts were one of the most common forms made in pressed glass. (WM)

39 *Miniature bowl.* 1830-50, New England; H. ¹⁵⁄₁₆″, Diam. 1¾″. Pressed glass. Stippled backgrounds, which added a quality of glitter or brilliance to glass and masked defects in the material, were characteristic of lacy pressed glass. (WM)

40 *Amethyst-colored compote,* probably Boston and Sandwich Glass Company. 1840-50, Boston, Massachusetts; H. 8¹⁄₁₆″, Diam. (top) 8⅝″. Pressed glass. (WM)

41 *Amber-colored tumbler.* 1860-80, America; H. 3⅜″, Diam. (top) 3¼″. Pressed glass. (WM)

42 *Dish.* Late nineteenth century, America; Diam. 9″. Pressed glass. This dish displays the same pattern as the bowl mold and reproduction bowl (cat. no. 18) that are also illustrated. (Courtesy Pennsylvania Historical & Museum Commission: Illustrated)

Dish. Late nineteenth century, America; Diam. 9″.

43 *Model of press,* J. Overmeyer. 1900, Corning, New York; L. 4″, H. 9½″, W. 8″. The model shows the type of pressing machinery used in the Corning Glass Works around 1900. (Courtesy The Corning Museum of Glass)

44 *Window pane.* 1800-40, America; L. 7⅞″, W. 7″. Blown crown process glass. So-called bull's-eye glass is the least desirable portion of a piece of crown glass. The bull's-eye is the mark of the pontil rod. (WM)

45 *Window pane,* Bakewell and Company. 1835-40, Pittsburgh, Pennsylvania; L. 6⁵⁄₁₆″, W. 4¹⁵⁄₁₆″. Marked. Pressed glass. The gothic motif of this window pane, a type used in door sidelights, lanterns, and glazed furniture doors, reflects the popularity of the gothic revival style and the adaptability of the pressing process to changing styles. (WM)

46 *Sugar bowl and lid.* 1900-20, America; H. 5½″, Diam. 4″. Pressed glass with daisy pattern. (HM: Displayed in shop front)

47 *Plate.* 1900-20, America; Diam. 11¾″. Pressed pattern glass. (HM: Displayed in shop front)

48 *Decanter with mushroom-shaped stopper.* 1830-40, probably America; H. 10″, Diam. 5″. Blown in a hinged, full-sized mold. Replacement stopper of pressed glass. (HM: Displayed in shop front)

49 *Decanter.* 1830-40, America; H. 8½″, Diam. 4½″. Blown in a hinged, full-sized mold. Shows a rough pontil mark. (HM: Displayed in shop front)

50 *Oil lamp base.* 1840-50, America; H. 9″. Pressed glass. (HM: Displayed in shop front)

51 *Set of four tumblers.* Nineteenth century, H. 3¾″, Diam. 3¼″. Pressed pattern glass. (HM: Displayed in shop front)

52 *Glassblower working at bench.* From Sidney Waugh, *The Art of Making Glass* (New York: Dodd, Mead & Co., 1937), opposite p. 16. (Courtesy Steuben Glass: Illustrated)

53 *Blowing goblets.* From Denis Diderot, *L'Encyclopédie, ou Dictionnaire Raisonné des Sciences, des Arts et des Métiers,* 11 vols. of plates (Paris: Briasson, 1762-72), 10: pl. 19, fig. 4.

54 *Pressing glass by machine.* From Apsley Pellatt, *Curiosities of Glass Making* (London: D. Bogue, 1849), p. 21. (Courtesy The Corning Museum of Glass: Illustrated)

VIII.   Silver: Handcrafted, Fused Plate, and Electroplate

Silver is second only to gold in being malleable and ductile. It can be pounded into sheets thinner than 1/100 of an inch or drawn into wire finer than human hair. These qualities made it possible for the silversmith to create many different forms using relatively simple tools. The silversmith depended on several different techniques to create a handcrafted silver object (25, illustrated).

The traditional method of forming hollow ware, such as a teapot or bowl, was by careful and repeated hammering in concentric circles on a disk of silver, a process called raising. Using a variety of hammers and stakes (a type of anvil), the silversmith gradually forced the metal to stretch and curve to the desired shape. Repeated hammering hardened the metal, and to restore its working qualities the object was heated until it was cherry red (annealing). It was then dipped into a mild acid solution to remove the fire stain (pickling).

A new method of forming hollow ware was widely adopted during the late eighteenth century. Thin sheets of silver were cut into pieces and joined by soldering the edges, a process called seaming. This was a much faster process, and it was quickly adapted to the new shapes of the neoclassical style. Improvements in rolling mills, which produced sheet silver from cast bars or ingots, made seaming commercially feasible.

Certain small forms such as flatware could be made by a hand process of die stamping. Spoons were often made with a two-part steel die. The upper part of the die was precisely cut to reproduce the front side of the spoon; the lower part was cut to reproduce the back side of the spoon. By placing a silver blank between the two halves of the die and hammering on the top, the silver assumed both the shape of the die and any decorative features cut into the die.

Small parts that could not be shaped conveniently by other means were usually cast in molds of sand or cuttlebone. Common

examples are the curved spouts on teapots, hinges for tankard lids, some handles, and decorative features. The parts were soldered to the main body or lid as required (12, illustrated).

The silversmith could decorate his wares with piercing, applied ornament, chasing, and engraving. Piercing involved cutting out small pieces of metal in order to create a decorative pattern; it was usually done with a fret saw or file after drilling a small hole. Applied ornament could be decorative bands of silver with a repeating pattern or small but elaborate castings, such as thumb-pieces on some tankards.

Chasing was the technique of decorating a thin metal surface by the skillful use of punches and small hammers. Punched from the outside, it is called chasing; punched from the inside, it is called repoussé. In more elaborate examples chasing and repoussé produced a three-dimensional effect. Coats of arms, names, initials, and dates were usually engraved, a process of cutting a small furrow in the surface to create thin, sharp lines.

The high cost of silver encouraged craftsmen to seek a convenient method of covering a less expensive metal with a thin coating of silver. The first commercially successful plating method was developed in Sheffield, England, in the 1740s; hence the popular term "Sheffield plate." It consisted of fusing under heat a thin bar of silver to a much thicker bar of copper; the ingot was then rolled into sheets with silver on one side and copper on the other. Where necessary both sides of the copper were plated.

Fused plate became the basis of a new industry distinct from the guild-dominated craft of the English silversmiths. Centered in Sheffield and Birmingham, fused-plate manufacturers at first concentrated on producing small objects such as buttons and buckles. During the late 1700s and early 1800s, the industry produced enormous quantities of larger wares that were very popular because of their handsome appearance and low cost (15, illustrated). The fused-plate industry died about 1850 as electroplated wares quickly took over its market.

Since the physical properties of copper are close to those of silver, fused plate could be worked by the hammer. Early examples of hollow ware were raised in the traditional manner. This slow and laborious method was soon replaced by seaming, a process of joining precut parts by soldering.

One of the most important contributions of the fused-plate industry was the development of mechanized die-stamping tech-

5 *Eighteenth-century goldsmith's shop* showing preparation of ingots and hand raising.

niques. At first limited to small parts and decorative elements, die stamping eventually made larger parts or whole pieces in one operation. Drop hammers could form a large tray or half a teapot in one drop (32, illustrated).

Instead of casting small parts in solid silver, the effect of casting was achieved by stamping two halves of a form, for example a finial or a handle. The halves were then filled with molten lead or solder and joined by soldering.

The traditional techniques of decorating silver were adopted by the fused-plate industry, but some needed modification to avoid exposing the copper beneath the silver. Piercing required the development of the fly punch, a tool that drew a burr of silver from the outer surface over the inner copper edge as it passed through the metal. A later improvement was a machine that pierced the pattern by punches stamping into metal beds. Engraving was first accomplished by cutting out the fused plate in the area to be engraved and soldering in its place a piece of sterling silver. About 1810 this technique was superseded by "rubbing in" thin shields of sterling silver, which provided sufficient depth to permit engraving without revealing the copper. Flat chasing by small hand punches imitated engraved lines without removing any silver. Swaging created decorative borders on trays and plates by a jaw-shaped tool that in effect crimped the edge when the top of the swage was hammered.

Electroplating techniques, which were rapidly adopted in the silver industry and soon replaced the more expensive fused- or Sheffield-plate process, evolved out of a series of discoveries and improvements. In 1794 the principle of the electric battery was discovered by Alessandro Volta, an Italian scientist. Two further steps—electrolysis (about 1800) and a dependable battery (about 1836)—were required before electroplating was commercially feasible.

In fused plate, silver was applied to the base metal before fabrication; in electroplate, silver was applied to the base metal after fabrication. Since electroplating is an electrochemical means of depositing one metal on another, an extremely small quantity of silver gave an object made from cheaper metal the appearance of solid silver (19, illustrated). In 1841 the Elkington Brothers of Birmingham, England, began to electroplate silver onto a cheap metal base thus permitting the production of attractive yet inexpensive tableware.

Stamping using a drop hammer.

12 *Teakettle, stand, and lamp* (silver),
    Edward Lownes. 1817-34,
    Philadelphia; H. (with handle
    down) 12¾".

5 *Teakettle, stand, and lamp* (silver
on copper). 1775-1800, Sheffield or
Birmingham, England; H. (with
handle up) 12½".

In electroplating silver, the cleaned metalware to be plated is connected as the cathode in a liquid known as the electrolyte, which contains silver in solution. Direct current, from batteries and later generators, is introduced through the anode, which consists of almost pure rolled silver. The silver in solution is electrically attracted to the metalware to be plated at the cathode, while the silver from the anode replaces the silver in the electrolyte. Although the time required for plating varies, an average procedure takes about four hours. The process required minimal hand labor, and since plating was the final step, all shaping and decorating techniques were done in the base metal.

The modern American silverware industry came into being in the mid-nineteenth century as manufacturers of britannia began to electroplate their wares. Britannia metal, an improved form of pewter introduced in America in the early nineteenth century, was first used as a base metal for electroplating. It was harder and brighter than pewter, and it could be formed by stamping and spinning while pewter could only be cast.

In the 1830s adoption of lathe spinning in britannia metal, fused plate, and sterling silver reduced the skilled hand labor necessary to form hollow ware. The workman started with a metal disk fixed in a lathe. Pressure carefully applied to the rotating disk gradually forced it against a wooden chuck of the desired cylindrical shape. Spinning was often used as a method of forming hollow ware in instances where a die was prohibitively expensive. A harder and whiter alloy of copper, nickel, and zinc, known as "nickel silver" or "German silver" slowly replaced britannia later in the nineteenth century.

Electroplating completely revolutionized the silverware industry. Fused plate ceased to be made. Sterling silver continued to be made, but the adoption of forming and decorative techniques associated with electroplating made most sterling production an adjunct of the plating industry (38, illustrated).

19 *Pitcher* (silver electroplated on copper and brass). 1840-60, probably England; H. 9¼".

1-6 *Silversmith's tools.* 1800-1900, America.

1 *Two planishing hammers* (steel and wood) for removing marks left by raising hammers. L. 9¾", W. 6¾"; (both). (Courtesy Colonial Williamsburg, Inc.)

2 *Jeweler's eyepiece.* H. 1½". (WM, funds for purchase, gift of Charles K. Davis)

3 *Nine punches for making punched decoration.* L. 2⅛"; L. 2¼"; L. 2⅛"; L. 2⁷⁄₁₆"; L. 2¼"; L. 1¼"; L. 1⁵⁄₁₆"; L. 1⅞"; L. 2⅛". (WM, funds for purchase, gift of Charles K. Davis; three courtesy Old Salem, Inc.)

4 *Two gravers for engraving.* L. 3¹¹⁄₁₆"; L. 3⅝". (WM, funds for purchase, gift of Charles K. Davis)

5 *Three blades for gravers.* L. 4¼"; L. 3⅝"; L. 2⅞". (WM, funds for purchase, gift of Charles K. Davis)

6 *Spoon* (silver) and three dies or punches (steel) used for forming spoon bowls, John Vogler. 1820-40, Salem, North Carolina; spoon: L. 6¹¹⁄₁₆"; dies: L. 7⁹⁄₁₆"; L. 5⅜"; L. 6". Compare with Diderot depiction of tools, cat. no. 26. (Courtesy Old Salem, Inc.)

7 *Spoon* (silver) and die (steel). Modern, America; spoon: L. 6½"; die: L. 8", W. 3", H. 6¾". (Courtesy Samuel Kirk & Son)

8 *Sample plate* (silver). Modern, America; Diam. 10⅞". The sample plate shows progressive stages of repoussé and chasing in creating a design. (Courtesy Samuel Kirk & Son)

9 *Salver* (silver), Jacob Hurd. 1740-56, Boston; Diam. 6¹⁵⁄₁₆". The hammered body is edged with molding cast in sections. The engraving of the coat of arms is a particularly fine example of this branch of the silversmith's art. (WM)

10 *Teapot* (silver), Joseph Richardson, Jr. 1790-1800, Philadelphia; H. 5½". This typical neoclassical form was seamed from sheet silver. The pierced gallery is a characteristic of Philadelphia silver of the period. (WM)

11 *Cream pitcher* (silver), Samuel Kirk. 1828, Baltimore; H. 8⅝". Overall chased decoration of high quality was characteristic of this silversmith who preserved hand techniques long after mechanization became widespread. (WM, gift of Dr. and Mrs. W. Tyler Haynes)

12 *Teakettle, stand, and lamp* (silver), Edward Lownes, 1817-34, Philadelphia; H. (with handle down) 12¾". Extravagant use of solid silver is evident in the heavy cast ornament on the stand. Compare with same form in fused plate, cat. no. 15. (WM: Illustrated)

13 *Pair of shoe buckles* (silver on brass). 1750-90, England; L. 2½", W. 3". Small objects like these buckles were the mainstay of the fused-plate industry in its early years. Brass was sometimes substituted for copper as the base metal. (WM, gift of Horace Porter)

14 *Candelabrum* (silver on copper). 1770-90, Sheffield or Birmingham, England; H. 15¾". (WM)

15 *Teakettle, stand, and lamp* (silver on copper). 1775-1800, Sheffield or Birmingham, England; H. (with handle up) 12½". Compare with the silver teakettle by Edward Lownes of Philadelphia, cat. no. 12. Engraving is simulated here by flat chasing; cast ornament is simulated by stamped sheet filled with solder. (WM: Illustrated)

16 *Tea urn* (silver on copper). 1775-1800, Sheffield or Birmingham, England; H. 18⅞". Silver has been removed from the cartouche leaving only the copper base. Possibly the original owner's arms or initials were removed by a later owner. The base is a good example of piercing in fused plate. (WM)

17 *Argand lamp* (silver on copper and silver on brass), Matthew Boulton. 1787-1809, Birmingham, England; H. 24½". The urn at the top was the oil tank for this innovative lighting device invented by Ami Argand in 1783. (WM)

18 *Oil lamp* (silver on copper). 1790-1810, England; H. 9¾". A silver shield was added to permit the engraving of the owner's initials. (WM)

19 *Pitcher* (silver electroplated on copper and brass). 1840-60, probably England; H. 9¼". The medieval motifs on this pitcher were probably stamped into sheet copper, which was electroplated after assembly of the various parts. A separate cylindrical interior and the handle are brass, the latter electroplated with silver. (Courtesy National Museum of History and Technology: Illustrated)

20 *Teapot* (silver electroplated on "nickel silver"). 1850-1900, probably England; H. 5½". Although similar in form and decoration to the silver teapot made 1790-1800 by Joseph Richardson, Jr., of

Philadelphia, cat. no. 10, the manufacturing processes and materials are quite different. (Anonymous lender)

21 *Soup tureen* (silver electroplated on britannia), Rogers, Smith and Company. 1862-77, New Haven, Connecticut; L. 15½″, H. 12″. The oval body was cast in two parts and soldered together. The entire piece was plated after attaching the cast handles and feet. (Anonymous lender)

22 *Tea urn* (silver electroplated on britannia), Wilcox Silver Plate Company. 1867-98, Meriden, Connecticut; H. 16½″. The body was formed by spinning on a lathe; the handles, feet, and spigot were cast. (Anonymous lender)

23 *Candelabra* (fused plate) with three lights. 1770-1800, England; H. 20″. (HM: Displayed in shop front)

24 *Five-piece tea service* (silver), Gale and Willis. About 1870, New York City; teapot: H. 8″; teapot stand: L. 7¼″; creamer: H. 5¾″; sugar bowl with cover: H. 6½″; wastebowl: H. 3¼″. Marked. The wastebowl is inscribed with nineteenth-century family christening dates. The revival-style tea service is embellished with punched decoration that simulates the handworked bright-cut decoration of Federal period pieces. (Anonymous lender: Displayed in shop front)

25 *Eighteenth-century goldsmith's shop* showing preparation of ingots and hand raising. From Denis Diderot, *L'Encyclopédie, ou Dictionnaire Raisonné des Sciences, des Arts et des Métiers*, 11 vols. of plates (Paris: Briasson, 1762-72), 8: pl. 1. (Illustrated)

26 *Eighteenth-century tools of the goldsmith.* From Denis Diderot, *L'Encyclopédie, ou Dictionnaire Raisonné des Sciences, des Arts et des Métiers*, 11 vols. of plates (Paris: Briasson, 1762-72), 8: pl. 11.

27 *Raising by hand.* From Frederick Bradbury, *History of Old Sheffield Plate* (London: Macmillan & Co., 1912), p. 110.

28 *Modern photograph showing hand chasing.* (Courtesy Samuel Kirk & Sons)

29 *Modern photograph showing hand engraving.* (Courtesy Samuel Kirk & Sons)

30 *Copper ingot* covered with silver sheet before plating by fusion process and copper ingot covered with silver sheet after plating. From Frederick Bradbury, *History of Old Sheffield Plate* (London: Macmillan & Co., 1912), pp. 12-13.

31 *Flatting mill* for rolling small pieces of sheet gold or silver. From Denis Diderot, *L'Encyclopédie, ou Dictionnaire Raisonné des Sciences, des Arts et des Métiers,* 11 vols. of plates (Paris: Briasson, 1762-72), 2: pl. 1 (detail).

32 *Stamping using a drop hammer.* From Frederick Bradbury, *History of Old Sheffield Plate* (London: Macmillan & Co., 1912), p. 104. (Illustrated)

33 *Swages* used in forming decorative borders. From Frederick Bradbury, *History of Old Sheffield Plate* (London: Macmillan & Co., 1912), p. 113.

34 *Punching and piercing machine and tray with pierced handles.* From Frederick Bradbury, *History of Old Sheffield Plate* (London: Macmillan & Co., 1912), p. 119.

35 *Beds and punches used in piercing machine.* From Frederick Bradbury, *History of Old Sheffield Plate* (London: Macmillan & Co., 1912), p. 120.

36 *Modern photograph showing machine spinning* of silver hollow ware. (Courtesy Samuel Kirk & Sons).

37 *Electroplating tank* installation with batteries, rheostat, and ammeter. (Constructed for exhibit).

38 *Nineteenth-century electroplated tea set.* From Reed and Barton, *Artistic Workers in Gold and Silver Plate* . . . (Springfield, Mass.: Reed and Barton, 1884), p. 35. (Illustrated)

39 *Electroplated toothpick holders.* From Reed and Barton, *Artistic Workers in Gold and Silver Plate* . . . (Springfield, Mass.: Reed and Barton, 1884), p. 189.

40 *Advertisement for electroplated Waterloo Medium Forks.* From *Silver-Plated Table-Ware* (Hartford, Conn.: William Rogers Manufacturing Co., 1886).

Nineteenth-century electroplated tea set.

Designed by
Malcolm Grear Designers, Inc.
Typeset by
Dumar Typesetting, Inc.
Printed by
Foremost Lithograph Co.
on Mohawk Superfine